CW00547884

Plastic S.....
its Origins

The Life and Works
of Sir Harold Gillies
1882 – 1960

RICHARD PETTY

First published in 2013 by Richard Petty,
32 Weymouth Street
London
W1G 7BU

Any copy of this book issued by the publisher as a paperback is sold
subject to the condition that it shall not by way of trade or otherwise
be lent, resold, hired out or otherwise circulated without the publisher's prior consent in any form of binding or cover other than that in
which it is published and without a similar condition including these
words being imposed on a subsequent purchaser.

First published in Great Britain in 2013

Copyright © 2013 Richard Petty, London

All rights reserved. No part of this book may be reproduced, stored, or
transmitted by any means— whether auditory, graphic, mechanical, or
electronic—without written permission of both publisher and author,
except in the case of brief excerpts used in critical articles and reviews.
Unauthorized reproduction of any part of this work is illegal and is
punishable by law.

ISBN 978-0-9926739-0-1

Designed and typeset by Dinah Drazin
Printed in Great Britain by T J International Ltd., Padstow, Cornwall
On Munken Lynx 120gsm
Typeset in Monotype Dante

SIR HAROLD DELF GILLIES

Knighted by King George V for work in the First World War and thereafter; also Military Commander of the Order of the British Empire, Commander of the Order of Dannebrog, Commander of the Order of St Olav, twice mentioned in war despatches (1914-1918); Fellow of the Royal College of Surgeons; Fellow (Honorary) of the American College of Surgeons, the Royal Australasian College of Surgeons; President of the First International Congress of Plastic Surgery (1955); Honorary Member Asociacion Medica Argentina, Société Belge de Chirurgerie, Colegio Brasileiro de Cirurgioes, Sociedad de Cirugios de Chile, Société Française de Chirurgie Plastique et Reconstructive, Die Berliner Medizinische Gesellschaft Ernennt, Scandinavian Association of Plastic Surgeons, Swedish Association of Plastic Surgeons, Société Vaudoise de Médecine Lausanne, American Association of Plastic Surgeons, American Dental Association, American Society of Plastic and Reconstructive Surgery.

Foreword

My father was a colleague of Harold Gillies, a fellow ENT surgeon, and was a great admirer of his achievements during the First World War and in establishing plastic surgery as a recognised discipline, let alone his astonishing gifts in the practice of the art.

Gillies was a Barts man. I had a place at Guy's to take up after Cambridge. I changed my mind, deciding I would be happier at Barts. Too late in applying, my father appealed to Gillies. With typical kindness, he used his influence to obtain an interview for me. Sadly he had died before I could meet him and thank him.

It was partly this association which gave me the idea of putting together an account of Sir Harold's life and work for my Wix Prize entry at Barts. This was in 1962.

Because of the close association that Barts had with Fleet Street, I had the privilege of access to the press cuttings and photographic libraries there. These were the days of card index systems. At Barts, paper notes for patients were still available from the 19th century onwards, and we had a magnificent library watched over by an inspirational librarian. All this has disappeared; destroyed or dispersed.

Therefore, my small contribution to the memory of this truly great man of medicine has, with the passage of time, become, by default, a unique record.

Obvious textual errors have, I hope, been edited out, but my student efforts remain much as they were, obviously now somewhat archaic in their form. However, I hope they give you a coherent account of the important contribution that Sir Harold Gillies made to the development of the art of surgery, and some inkling of his intriguing personality.

Viola Fort and Lucy Scholes have been responsible for putting the original manuscript into a printable format and for the general editing: my very grateful thanks to them.

1882 – 1914

Harold Delf Gillies was born on June 17th, 1882 to Robert and Emily Gillies of Dunedin, New Zealand. Robert Gillies was by profession a land and estate agent and represented his local community in the House of Representatives. His wife Emily, née Street, was of English descent, a member of the Street family of Birtley near Guildford.

Harold's childhood was marked by the early development of the characteristics of temperament which were to play such an important part in his future career. His first love was woodcarving, a pastime upon which he lavished many hours of patient work. Patience is a rare attribute in the very youthful, but not only was his work meticulously detailed, it also showed no uncertain degree of artistic merit.

At the age of thirteen, he left his local school to become a boarder at Wanganui College, one of New Zealand's most distinguished public schools. Here he quickly developed athletic tendencies, and with encouragement and coaching, exhibited great promise and proficiency in cricket, golf and rowing. His success at golf and cricket were helped by a natural sense of timing and a good eye for the ball, and his proudest achievement at Wanganui was his captaincy of the school cricket XI.

Perhaps understandably, the young Harold's academic

career suffered in the shadow of his sporting achievements: a maximum of time, effort and energy was expended perfecting the technique and fitness required to play those sports to his own satisfaction. Despite this (or, more likely, due to this) he was awarded a place at Gonville and Caius College[1], Cambridge, to study Natural Sciences. Some have unjustly referred to this as a 'sports scholarship', but Harold Gillies had a very real wish to become qualified in medicine.

Having taken up his place at Caius, the 'medical college' of Cambridge, in October 1903, he quickly asserted his presence on the sports field, spurred by the added incentive of stiffer competition. In his own words, "I went up with the idea of playing cricket", but in fact, his first success came when he was asked to play golf for the University. His golfing prowess had been discovered entirely by chance during a rest period whilst training with the Cambridge Boat Race crew. He remained a playing member of the Cambridge Golf team for the entire three years of his residence.

A typical perfectionist, he abandoned his interest in cricket to concentrate on the more taxing sport of rowing, and in 1904 was rewarded by being invited to row No. 7 for the winning Cambridge crew in the Boat Race.

Gillies soon gained a reputation as a wit with a distinctly bizarre sense of humour (one cannot help but wonder how much of this, along with his artistic flair, was due to his

---

1 Gonville Hall, founded on June 4th, 1349 by the Reverend Edmund Gonville. Gonville and Caius College incorporated on September 4th, 1557 by Dr John Caius, President of the College of Physicians 1555 – 1563, practising in the parish of St Bartholomew-the-Less. Physician to King Edward IV.

maternal great great uncle, Edward Lear). It is a tribute to the stability of his character that these personal successes, and the subsequent worship of a sports-loving generation of students, did nothing to corrupt his extrovert personality and self-assurance with unbearable conceit. Thanks to his strength of character and genuine humility, Gillies always retained the respect, admiration and friendship of those who were close to him. On first meeting, he would give the impression of a quiet and courteous man, not at all the broad, rough-tongued Kiwi that might have been expected.

Gillies graduated from Cambridge in 1905, having gained a second-class honours degree in the Natural Sciences Tripos, and entered the Medical College of St Bartholomew's Hospital in London, following in the footsteps of innumerable other Caians and distinguished members of the medical profession.

At Barts the new burden of work necessarily curtailed his sporting activities, but Gillies managed to retain an active interest in rowing and golf, which he played for England against Scotland whilst still a student in 1908.

During his student days at Barts he shared a flat with four of his Cambridge contemporaries at 26 St James's Square in Holland Park, where he paid forty shillings a week for his board and residence. At one stage, the students were faced with the threat of eviction when the owners of the house gave the landlord notice to quit, prior to the sale of the property. Always quick to size up a situation, Gillies organised a syndicate. The members of the household bought the flat, retaining the landlord as a general factotum.

If Gillies missed a day's training with the Boat Club he would disappear after breakfast with the words, "Just off for a few swings", whereafter he could be found perched on a stool in his bedroom practising rowing exercises. He always managed to keep fit despite enjoying wholeheartedly the good things in life. Considering this ardent pursuit of social and sporting interests, Gillies' academic career remained good, if not impeccable. He always impressed his teachers with a mental agility and ingenuity which probably covered many gaps in his knowledge of medicine at that time.

After his qualification, MRCS, LRCP, in 1908, he became, in common with all other former medical students, a responsible member of the medical profession overnight. He was appointed to the house and became Sir D'Arcy Power's[2] junior house surgeon on the Light Blue firm.

It was during this period, under the shrewd and friendly eye of Sir D'Arcy, that Gillies' interest in surgery flowered and became to him "a way of life". He also discovered his attraction to otorhinolaryngology and determined that it was in this that he wanted to specialise. In 1909 he was awarded the Luther Holden[3] Scholarship for research in surgery. At that time, no medical house job was required of a prospective surgeon in order to fulfil his preregistration commitments, so he continued to serve Sir D'Arcy

2 Sir D'Arcy Power, FRCS, KBE 1855 – 1941. Qualified SBH 1882. Appointed Surgeon SBH 1904. Appointed consulting surgeon and archivist SBH 1920. Appointed Governor of SBH 1920. Prolific writer on the history of surgery and SBH.
3 Luther Holden – Surgeon to the SBH 1865 – 1879.

Power as a senior house surgeon. However, towards the end of this appointment, he was offered the post of medical officer to an expedition travelling to Egypt in search of the lost Tomb of the Kings. Here was an irresistible chance to see some of the world before he was overtaken by the inevitable ties of practising surgery. He was given permission to relinquish the remaining two months of his appointment and join the expedition. The expedition returned empty handed, but his time in Egypt had proved invaluable, broadening his outlook and giving him a lifelong taste for travel.

It was in 1910, at the age of 28, that he was elected FRCS and appointed surgical assistant to Sir Milsom Rees[4], a post he retained until 1915. He was subsequently appointed Surgeon to the Ear, Nose & Throat Department of the Prince of Wales General Hospital in Tottenham, and Pathologist to the Throat Hospital in Soho's Golden Square.

In 1911, Gillies married Kathleen Margaret Jackson.

Despite his heavy professional commitments, he still pursued the game of golf, and, in 1913, won his highest award in that field by taking the Royal St George's Grand Challenge Vase, the most valuable golfing trophy in the world, in face of competition from the best amateur golfers in the United Kingdom.

---

4 Sir Milsom Rees, FRCS, CVO. Qualified SBH 1889. Laryngologist to HM Queen Alexandra, to HM Household, to the Royal Opera House, Covent Garden and to the Guildhall School of Music.

1914 – 1916

War is the only true stimulant to progress – H.G. Wells

The outbreak of hostilities against the German Empire in 1914 found Harold Gillies pursuing the accepted and comfortable course towards his final goal: the achievement of a consultantship in otolaryngological surgery. His work for Sir Milsom Rees brought him in contact with a rich and cultured world which he had previously not experienced, and he numbered among his patients Alfred de Rothschild and Dame Nellie Melba.

By 1915 many of his colleagues had volunteered as medical officers to the British Expeditionary Force in France. Gillies realised, in common with many others at this period, that the Government's promise of a quick victory was over-optimistic. The war came to a sanguinary standstill in the trenches, the British Expeditionary Force expanded into Kitchener's 2nd Army, and medical officers were in great demand to deal with the thousands of casualties[5] pouring daily into the casualty clearing stations and base hospitals.

Gillies volunteered early in 1915 and was commissioned into the Royal Army Medical Corps with the rank of

---

5 Of the 56,000,000 men called to arms during the First World War, 26,000,000 became casualties.

Captain. He was immediately posted to France, to the base hospital at Wimereux, well behind the line of battle, where he took up general surgical duties. Wimereux was within earshot of heavy gunfire from the forward areas, and the dull, soul-destroying routine of wound surgery in those days combined to make his life a constant frustration. He longed to find some more active job, an understandable feeling in one who had been so active all his life.

It was in this atmosphere that the first seeds of his inspiration were sown, seeds which grew and flowered into a massive undertaking which was not only to affect Gillies' life but the lives of many thousands of suffering men, the pathetic, broken products of the holocaust of war.

On landing in France at Boulogne, Gillies met the dental surgeon Sir Charles Valadier. Sir Charles was campaigning among his more influential patients for the institution of plastic and jaw units to treat the many facial wounds caused by the devastating effects of shrapnel. It was whilst Gillies was serving at the base hospital that Sir Charles was given his first unit in Wimereux and he was invited to assist at the first operation performed in it.

A close friend of Gillies', the American Dr C.W. Roberts, arrived at Wimereux having spent six months with the American Ambulance in Paris where he observed and participated in the jaw surgery performed there. He brought back with him a book recently published by the German surgeon, Lindemann, who, it was reported, had miraculously patched up many hideously mutilated soldiers sufficiently well to send back to the war machine.

His time at Wimereux, along with these reports of

pioneering surgical advances emerging from the theatre of war, opened Gillies' eyes to the pressing need for the utilisation of plastic surgery, not only to the advantage of the British war effort, but also to that of the thousands of wounded so disfigured that their living would be more of a pain to them than their dying.

In June 1915 Gillies spent his leave in Paris. Armed with an introduction from a colleague, he visited the Martinique surgeon Hippolyte Morestin, who was working in the Val-de-Grace Hospital. Gillies heard rumours that Morestin was doing for French soldiers what Lindemann was doing for the German. He was not disappointed. Morestin was only too pleased to demonstrate to the young surgeon the techniques he had developed in *chirurgèrie plastique*, and showed him in particular an operation for removal of a cancer of the face with subsequent plastic repair of the tissue defect. Gillies was delighted: in his own words, "It so thrilled me that I fell in love there and then."

It was apparent that similar techniques to those he had seen performed and had read about could readily be put to use, but he was shocked that there was so little attention paid to the cosmetic result of the operations. Gillies determined that, should the chance occur for him to practise this surgery, as much regard would be given to the appearance as the physical function of the repaired soldier.

He returned to Wimereux with one object in mind: to persuade his superiors that there was a vital need for the institution of specialist hospitals in England to deal with the problems of facial surgery.

Gillies was lucky in having as chiefs two highly

sympathetic and broadminded men, Sir Anthony Bowlby[6] and Sir John Rose Bradford[7], who had distinguished themselves in civilian practice before the war. Both men were impressed by Gillies' arguments and enthusiasm, and as a result, contacted Lieutenant General Sir Alfred Keogh[8], Director General, Home Medical Service, to enquire about the possibility of instituting a pilot surgery unit in England.

By the end of 1915 Gillies had been recalled to England, and in conjunction with Colonel Sir William Arbuthnot Lane[9], Director of the Cambridge Hospital in Aldershot, plans were made for the experimental unit. Thanks to an amazing feat of organisation, the first operation was performed by Gillies in the completed unit at the Cambridge Hospital, Aldershot, during the February of 1916.

6 Sir Anthony Alfred Bowlby, Bt., FRCS, KCMG, KCVO, KCB 1855-1924. Qualified SBH 1876. Appointed consulting surgeon SBH 1919. Appointed consulting surgeon BEF 1914/2nd Army 1915. Subsequently General Adviser to the Director General, Army Medical Service.

7 Sir John Rose Bradford, Bt., FRCP, KCMG, CB, CBE, 1863-1935. Qualified UCH, 1881. Appointed physician UCH 1900. Appointed consulting physician BEF 1914/2nd Army 1915. Neurophysiologist of distinction.

8 Lieutenant General Sir Alfred Keogh, FRCP, FRCS (Hon.), GCB, GCVO, CH, 1857-1936. Director General Home Medical Services 1914-1916.

9 Sir William Arbuthnot Lane, Bt., FRCS, CB, 1856 – 1943. Qualified Guy's 1872. Appointed surgeon Guy's 1888. Consulting surgeon to the Aldershot Command 1914-1918. Organised and opened Queen Mary's Hospital, Sidcup.

1916 – 1918

War is the only proper school for a surgeon – Hippocrates

Gillies threw himself into the challenging work of plastic surgery with enormous drive and enthusiasm. His knowledge, in fact, was very little at this time and he was compelled to rely upon his own experience of general and otolaryngolocical surgery, and the sparse published work that was available.

Plastic surgery is an ancient art with roots that run deep into history. It flourished during times of war, and it was the greatest war that man had ever witnessed that caused its rebirth and growth to maturity.

Few men in recent times had treated plastic surgery as anything except a cosmetic aid to appearance, below the dignity of any self- respecting surgeon. Gillies had to turn to the literature of the earliest writers; to Celsus, to the Sushruta Samhita and to Gaspare Tagliacozzi[10] to find accounts of successful procedures. From those men, and from the published work of such more or less contemporary surgeons as C Nélaton of France (1807 – 1873), Karl Thiersch[11] of Germany and Keegan and Smith of India,

10 *Vide: History of Plastic Surgery* below.
11 Karl Thiersch. Professor of Surgery at Erlangen and Leipzig. Revolutionised practice of modern plastic surgery by invention of skin graft, described at a meeting of German Surgical Society in 1874. For von Graefe and Nélaton *vide History of Plastic Surgery* below.

all contemporaries, and Carl Ferdinand Von Graefe (1787 – 1840), he garnered sufficient data upon which to base his first principles.

The first months at Aldershot were spent in trying every known method and technique mentioned in the literature. He was surprised to find that many of the methods described in modern times tended to be unsuccessful unless based on ancient principles devised by the classical surgeons. As Gillies said in 1923, "There is hardly an operation – hardly a single flap – in use today that has not been suggested a hundred years ago." His own work was original, of course, in that plastic surgery had to be built up again *de novo*.

Gradually, a pattern evolved, and with great ingenuity and imagination, he applied successful techniques to each surgical problem as it presented, adapting and extemporising as operations progressed. After many disappointments and false alarms, and after much hard-won experience had been gained, Gillies was able to formulate a series of 'principles', which, if correctly applied, would yield reliable results. These principles were not, in fact, inflexible rules by which the plastic surgeon was to be governed, but merely techniques, the use of which in solving a specific problem would not ensure success, but would increase the chances of success of the operation considerably.

Before the war the implantation of foreign substances had been practised and advised for the reconstruction of the facial skeleton, but Gillies rightly deduced from the lowness of the short-term survival rate that the long-term survival rate of these heterogenous grafts would be even worse. "There is no royal road to the fashioning of the facial scaffold by artificial means, the surgeon must tread the hard and narrow way of pure surgery," Gillies declared in 1920. All his techniques utilised living tissues from the body of the afflicted patient.

By the end of 1916, Gillies felt that he and his team of nursing staff and assistants were sufficiently proficient to run a plastic surgery unit independent of the limiting confines of the Cambridge Hospital. Sir William Arbuthnot Lane, recognising the potentialities of this branch of surgery in the treatment of war wounds, pressed the Red Cross to find Gillies a site for a new specialist hospital. A committee, including Lady Nelson and Lady Keynes, was formed to help negotiations in this matter and, as Gillies remarked, "had such social and political prestige that the War Office gave us permission to move to a new and larger premises."

The team which was to undertake the move consisted of Nurse Catherine Black heading the all-important nursing staff; the Chief Dental Surgeon Captain C.A.B. King, aided by A. L. Fraser and joined subsequently by Captain Kelsey Fry MC[12]; the chief radiologist, Captain H. Multrea Johnston; a lay photographer, Sidney Walbridge; and an assistant surgeon, Lieutenant J. Edwards, who was responsible for the preparation of the plaster casts necessary for the planning of each operation.[13] Other lay members of the unit were E.F. Greenway and R. Seymour, both of whom

12 Sir William Kelsey Fry, FRCS, CBE, MC, Qualified Guy's 1912. Dental Surgeon Guy's Hospital. Senior Dental Surgeon Queen's Hospital, Sidcup and East Grinstead.

13 *Vide* 'Works'.

had been among Gillies' first patients and had stayed on to help with the organisation of the complicated filing system which had developed. The former had been a business writer for the *Daily Express* before the war, to which he returned at the end of hostilities, but the latter, 'Big Bob' Seymour, remained Gillies' devoted friend and secretary for forty years. Last, but by no means the least important, was Professor Henry Tonks, Principal of the Slade School of Art, who had volunteered for service, and, although too old to fight, had been given clerical duties with the rank of full Lieutenant. It was behind a desk that Gillies discovered Professor Tonks, a most distinguished artist in his own right, and persuaded him to help the unit by making a permanent record in diagrammatic and sketch form of all operations performed. In this way it was possible for Gillies to correlate known techniques with extemporisation and hence, through a series of cases, to be able to develop and find inspiration for new methods.

The Red Cross, with War Office sanction, responded rapidly to Sir William Arbuthnot Lane's entreaties for a hospital building by requisitioning Frognal, the home of the Earl of Sidney, and erecting a complex but well-planned system of hutted wards within its grounds outside Sidcup.

Under the command of Lieutenant Colonel J. R. Colvin, and in its new and salubrious surroundings, the unit expanded rapidly. Many novel procedures were devised and evolved during the unit's residence in the ordered atmosphere of Frognal, but the most important development was the rationalisation of plastic surgery as a positive entity within the framework of surgery itself. It was also at this time, through dire necessity, that the concept of rehabilitation and convalescence for plastic surgery cases was born.

As the war laboured on, beds became increasingly scarce and some method of 'parking' ambulant patients between operations had to be devised. Gillies was told of Parkwood, an unused mental hospital on Swanley Hill, which stood empty but staffed. He arranged that patients should be moved from Frognal to Parkwood as soon as they were fit, and there await the next stage in their reconstruction. This proved successful not only in relieving the acute congestion at Frognal, but also in occupying the many dull days of waiting that the soldiers had to endure.

Eventually, however, the unit outgrew the 320 beds at Frognal and was moved, on August 18th 1917, to Queen Mary's Hospital in Sidcup. No sooner had the unit arrived in their new home than the substantial flow of patients was suddenly and shockingly increased. The opening days of the Battle of the Somme produced unbelievable numbers of casualties. Within the space of ten days, over 2000 patients were admitted, arriving in convoys of up to 500; men starving, emaciated and weak from the arduous three day journey across France and England, many still caked with the mud of Flanders. The staff worked day and night to give preliminary treatment to the injured, to encourage primary healing and to cover extensive tissue loss with grafts. This nightmare of effort near overwhelmed the resources of the unit at a most critical stage in its development, but the tenacity of Gillies' team prevailed and the crisis passed. Now remained the long process of reconstructing body and mind of the shattered *mutilés*.

To accommodate the extra patients a ramp extension

was built onto Queen Mary's Hospital which housed 200 additional beds. The problem of finding new staff to deal with the influx had now to be tackled. Sir John Goodwin, who had replaced Sir Alfred Keogh as Director General of the Home Medical Service, had had the foresight to allow Gillies to keep the nucleus of staff he had trained at Frognal, despite the acute shortage of qualified surgeons in more general fields of work. He now recruited surgeons from member colonies of the British Empire, and Gillies was joined by Major Waldron and Captain Risdon from Canada, Colonel Newland from Australia and Major Pickerill from New Zealand. An American unit of 'observers and advisers' also followed and included Ivy and Ferris Smith who went on to introduce plastic surgery to medical practice in the United States after the war. The great American surgeon Vilray Papin Blair[14] also spent some months with the unit at Frognal and had given them much constructive advice.

There existed an atmosphere of friendly competition and cooperation, described by Captain T. Pomfret Kilner as "intellectual fervour and surgical enthusiasm". Gillies passed on to these men the accumulated knowledge won during the months at Aldershot and Frognal. He was a good but exacting teacher; his criticism was often cruelly destructive and outspoken, but was always followed by useful and kindly advice. A total of eight British surgeons and dental surgeons eventually passed through Sidcup and hence Gillies was responsible for the teaching of the first

14 Vilray P. Blair had written in 1912 a revolutionary work on 'The Surgery and Diseases of the Mouth and Jaws'.

generation of plastic surgeons in Great Britain.

Gillies' greatest personal achievement during these two years was the conception and development of the tubed pedicle flap, a procedure which overcame the limitations imposed by the simple free graft. This technique in the transference of tissues from one part of the body to another had been directly inspired by the work of 16th-century surgeon Gaspare Tagliacozzi. Gillies' own contributions to the technique included an original and ingenious method of blepharoplasty to cure ectropion of the eyelid due to scar contracture and many variations of existing techniques, especially those of Esser, converting cumbersome methods into neat, practicable operations. Great advances were also made in the fields of radiology, dental surgery and, particularly, anaesthetics under the gifted influence of Ivan Magill.[15]

On December 3rd 1917, Gillies read a paper to the Medical Society of London outlining his work and describing the ethics of plastic surgery within the realm of war. He stated that his first duty was to the Services – "to send back to duty as many soldiers as possible in the shortest time"; his second duty was to the patient, to do all that was in his power to give back that which had been lost and to restore morale and self-respect; and his third duty was to "the science and knowledge of surgery." He observed that the ful-

15 Sir Ivan Whiteside Magill, FRCS, KCVO, Sen. Anaesthetist Westminster Hospital / Brompton Hospital. Cons. Anaesthetist King George's Hospital, Ilford / St Andrew's Hospital, Dollis Hill / Admiralty / Ministry of Health / Royal National Hospital for Diseases of the Chest.

filment of all these duties concurrently was the most difficult problem the plastic surgeon had to face. During his talk he remarked, with characteristic humility, "I often wish that a better surgeon than myself had had the chances that have come my way."

By the time Armistice was signed in 1918, 11,000 patients had passed through his hands. The last patient did not leave his care until late in 1921 and incredibly, only ten of these eleven thousand were considered by the Ministry of Pensions as incurably disfigured.

Gillies was twice mentioned in Dispatches and was decorated with the Order of the British Empire for valuable services to his country in 1919, and was promoted CBE (Military) in 1920.

Shrapnel from the Western Front

Case 338 from
Plastic Surgery of the Face

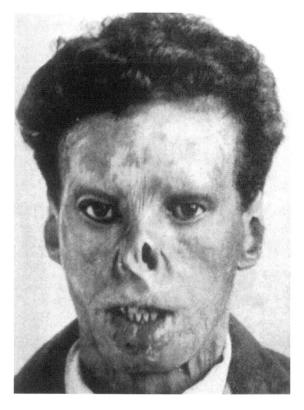

Healed state of burns suffered by Able Seaman Vicarage at Battle of Jutland, October 3rd, 1917, showing marked ectropion of eyelids and lips.

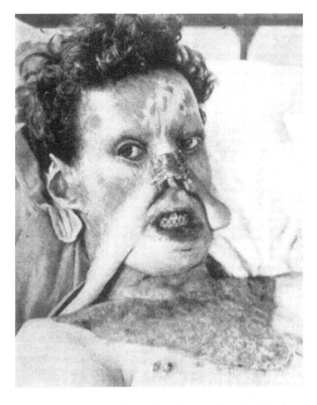

Tubed pedicles raised from the chest and applied to lower part of face. This was the first tubed pedicle operation performed by Sir Harold Gillies.

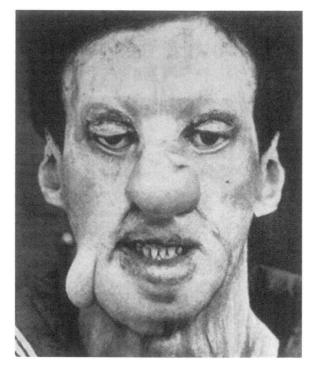

After epithelial outlay to upper eyelids, construction of new nose (lymphoedematous) and return of left tubed pedicle.

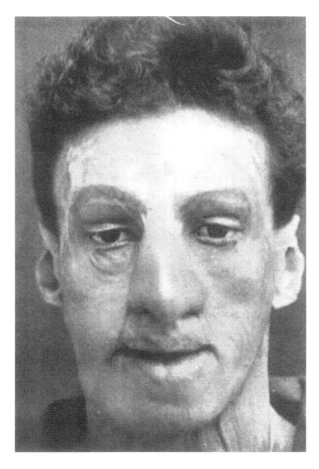

Final appearance. Eyebrows are free grafts.

1919 – 1930

Sapiens qui Prospicit – Motto of Malvern College

1919 was a sad year for Gillies. The team of surgeons at Sidcup quickly disintegrated, members returning either to their pre-war specialities, or, in the case of those from the Dominions, to their native countries. It was to replace this loss that the War Office appointed a newly qualified surgeon, Captain Thomas Pomfret Kilner, to the unit at Queen Mary's. This was the beginning of a close association that lasted until 1930.

Gillies now had two alternatives open to him. Sir Milsom Rees had promised that he could return to the assistantship he had left in 1915, which would have guaranteed Gillies both security and financial and professional success. "There was an enticing position waiting for me in my previous ENT speciality," Gillies remembers, "but in plastic surgery there was only a nebulous future. Would there be good work and enough of it, or would I become a mere cosmetician?" The second alternative was to apply to his old hospital, St Bartholomew's, for an assistantship, where despite the relatively junior position, he would at least have the chance of practising some plastic surgery.

With little regret but much soul-searching, Gillies decided to abandon the world that Sir Milsom Rees offered him –

the world of celebrities and royalty, and contacted St Bartholomew's. He was immediately offered a choice of two posts: that of an assistant in general surgery with a chance of practising plastic surgery on the side, or that of chief assistant to the Ear, Nose and Throat Department with the certain opportunity of being able to concentrate wholeheartedly on plastic surgery. Not surprisingly he accepted the latter with alacrity.

In the meantime he had been invited to visit America by the many friends who had spent time at Sidcup. Gillies was glad to escape the atmosphere of reaction and anti-climax in post-war England, and armed with seven hundred slides, he undertook the long sea journey.

During the first week of his visit he received what he admitted was a "bitter blow". He learnt that Filatoff, the ophthalmologist working in Odessa, had forestalled him in the publication of the tubed pedicle method of transferring tissues. Although Gillies realised that any surgeon aware of the problems of grafting would sooner or later conceive the idea of the tubed pedicle, the discovery was nevertheless hugely frustrating.

The full weeks of visiting and lecturing helped him to recover from this severe disappointment. He first presented his slides illustrating the work at Sidcup at a surgical dental meeting in Chicago. He then visited the Mayo brothers at their Clinic in Rochester and Vilray Blair in St Louis. There followed in quick succession a lecture to the American Dental Association in New Orleans and an address to a surgical meeting in New York with his Canadian colleagues Risdon and Waldron as companions. The final weeks were spent visiting Kazanjian[16] in Boston, Ivy and Dorrance in Philadelphia, Sheehan in New York and Logan in Chicago.

Throughout these travels, Gillies was subject to the acclaim and praise of the American medical profession. His lectures were an unqualified success and his own personal charm had endeared him to many he had not known previously. In his own words, "The trip brought home to me, and I may say to my American colleagues, that, at Queen's Hospital, Sidcup, we had witnessed the organisation of a new surgery. The justification for such a bold assertion lies in the fact that plastic surgery had passed from the empirical to a stage based on sound principles."

Gillies returned to England encouraged by the enthusiastic response of the American medical world to plastic surgery, and confident that it would meet with an equally good reception in England. The first show of this confidence arrived in his appointment as surgeon in charge of the newly formed plastic surgery department at the Prince of Wales Hospital, Tottenham, the first civilian plastic surgery unit in England.

In 1920 his book *Plastic Surgery of the Face* was published by the Oxford University Press and Hodder and Stoughton. This was a collected and edited account of the work performed between the years 1915 and 1919. Gillies had had little time to produce papers during the war and so many of the procedures described in the book were entirely novel to its readers. It was not only acclaimed by the medical pro-

---

16 Kazanjian had been responsible for the preliminary treatment of many casualties in the French Jaw Unit before their transfer to Sidcup.

fession itself but also by the lay public, and many enthusiastic reports were published in the daily press. It marked a monumental development in the field of surgery and confirmed the reputation that Gillies had gained during the war.

Extract from notes of Henry Causer (M 11211) before discharge, November 1923

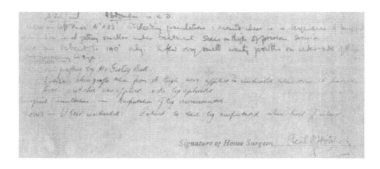

Extract from notes of Henry Causer (M 11211), 'Surgical consultations - amputation of leg recommended', April 1922

Gillies' chief at Barts, Mr Douglas Harmer[17], was most enthusiastic about finding work for his assistant. Gillies joked he was "the scrap basket for the whole hospital" with some justification, since many patients were referred to him as a last resort. For instance, in December 1922 he was asked to see a young man, nineteen years of age, who had had an incapacitating ulcer on the left knee for seven years and had been readmitted for amputation. A series of attempts to graft the ulcer using the Thiersch method had been attempted over the years and all had failed. Gillies, over a period of eleven months, succeeded in giving the boy full movement to his knee by using his tubed pedicle technique. Cases such as these led to the full acceptance of plastic surgery at Barts, but many years passed before it was deemed necessary to elect a consultant in this speciality.

17 William Douglas Harmer, MC, FRCS. Qualified SBH 1899. Surgeon Throat Department and Lecturer in Diseases of the Throat SBH.

Gillies had had a number of private patients in the wards at Sidcup during the war, and by 1922 his private practice was growing healthily. He shared rooms at this time with Kilner at 7-9 Portland Place and they travelled many miles together from these headquarters. The work was hard and they operated for long hours at a time at Sidcup, Roehampton, Barts and Tottenham. One of Gillies' vivid memories of this period was the immense weight of the bags of special instruments they had to transport from one hospital to another.

The practice was helped by the occasional cases of deformed noses for rhinoplasty and old secondary harelips for buccal inlays. These two techniques were Gillies' specialities and surgeons and practitioners were only too pleased to refer such cases to his care. It was during this period that he developed his technique for face-lifting, but he did little to encourage patients to undergo this treatment as he was afraid of being dubbed a 'beauty surgeon' at this most critical stage in the growth of the practice.

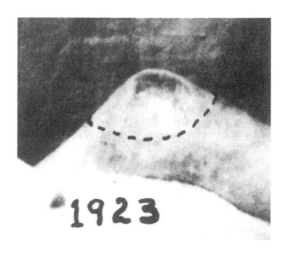

Henry Causer, M 11211:
Ulcer (after excision of fungating naevus) on left knee, 1923.

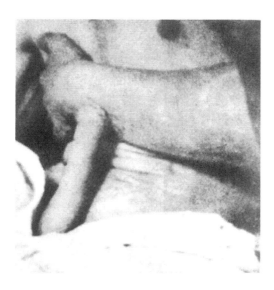

Tubed pedicle raised from abdomen and attached to left wrist.
The base was later severed and applied to defect on knee.

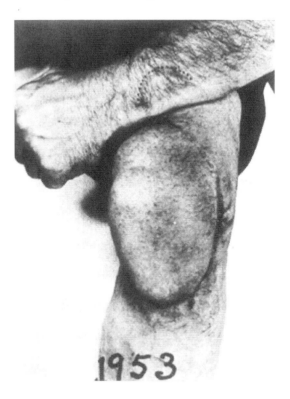

Condition of knee in 1953. The knee is completely mobile.

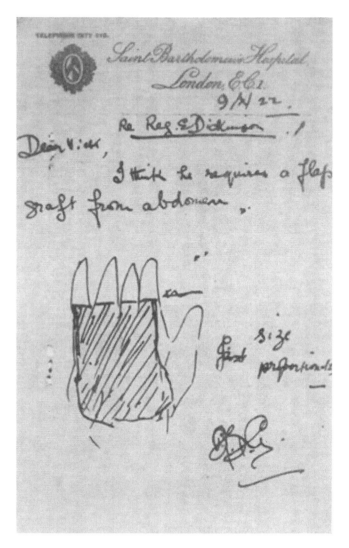

Advisory letter to Mr R.M. Vick concerning Reginald Dickson (M10803) who was suffering from scar contracture of left hand following third degree burns, October 1922.

In 1923 he accepted his first student, Albert Davies. Davies was the first in a long line of plastic surgeons who joined Gillies for periods of a year or more in order to "drink from the fount of knowledge". Each student paid a £100 token training fee, and in return for this, shadowed Gillies into all hospitals and private clinics he visited in the course of his work.

Before he finally left France in 1916, Gillies had visited Morestin a second time at the Val-de-Grace Hospital in Paris. For some inexplicable reason Morestin had refused point-blank to see him. This disappointment stayed with him and it was for this reason he always went out of his way to help students himself. "Teaching has always been a joy," he remarked, and this enthusiasm benefited a whole generation of British plastic surgeons.

In the March of 1924 the world was shocked by a tragic incident at sea. The Royal Danish Naval Ship *Geysir*, whilst carrying out smoke-screen experiments off Copenhagen, was gutted by fire caused by the explosion of a phosphorus bomb. The blast itself killed many sailors but a total of sixty severe burn cases resulted from flash, phosphorus and fire. Gillies had been visited the previous year by a Danish surgeon who had watched him operate at Sidcup, and as a result of this contact he was asked to visit Denmark to treat the injured.

Gillies travelled to Copenhagen and worked for two weeks giving primary treatment, covering widespread tissue loss with grafts and protecting healthy eyes by sewing together the seared lids. On April 3rd after the preliminary work had been completed, he was received by King Christian. He was accompanied by a Danish naval attaché to the

Royal Palace and spent half an hour in audience. Gillies discussed the nature of the operations with the King and presented him with a copy of *Plastic Surgery of the Face*. He was decorated with the red and white ribbon of the Order of Dannebrog for his valuable services to the Danish people. Over the next couple of years, the injured Danish seamen visited Gillies in England to undergo the completion of their repairs.

Golf was still his main pleasure and pastime and in 1924 he was ranked tenth in the amateur golfing world. He introduced the use of wooden tees some time before, which measured between five and fifteen inches in height, when the vast majority of golfers were still using piles of sand off which to drive. He achieved great accuracy and power with his flat swing and was a much sought-after player at his two clubs, Eye and Woking. In fact, he caused a sensation in the sporting world when he used a beer bottle tee at Woking during an important match as the ground was too hard to take his wooden one!

Gillies had also taken up fishing and was fast becoming a very accomplished fly-fisher. He belonged to the Houghton Club at Stockbridge on the river Test, which is famed for trout in its higher and salmon in its lower reaches. He delighted in the game of stalking the large, old trout and found the sport an ideal form of relaxation.

*Sir Harold and his son Michael practising putting in their
garden at Church Oakley, near Basingstoke.*
By kind permission of Thomson Newspapers Ltd.

It was during this period that Gillies seriously discussed the
possibility of instituting a 'flying plastic surgeon' organisation. Air travel was now becoming feasible with larger
and more reliable machines being produced, and passen-
ger lines were growing rapidly. Gillies found that his services were called for in many parts of the country, especially
during the hunting season, and his plans for equipping a
plane to carry a team of anaesthetist, nurse and plastic sur-

geon would have no doubt met with enthusiastic approval. He found, however, with the increasing dimensions of his practice, less and less time to indulge in such ambitious schemes. In 1924, however, he was honoured with the position of consulting plastic surgeon to the Royal Air Force, a post that he held until 1938 when he was succeeded by Sir Archibald McIndoe.

By 1927 Gillies felt himself sufficiently secure and well-established in his work to practise fully the techniques in cosmetic surgery that he had developed. This controversial aspect of plastic surgery was claimed by many in the medical profession to be both unethical and unnecessary, but Gillies defended it, saying, "It is easy to agree to do a beauty operation but not always quite so easy to be certain it is justified. A frightful looking old girl comes in for a face lift; a deep swallow is taken before surgery is begun for it is obvious even after the most wonderful face lift she will still look like the North Pole. That is only to us, not to her. She is tickled with any improvement. Often while lifting a face I have had the feeling of guilt that I am merely making money. Yet...is it not justified if it brings even a little extra happiness to a soul who well needs it? The less they have the more they appreciate the little we can do for them - this is a plastic surgeon's ode to an ugly woman, but a woman." He later added, "Certainly a beautiful woman is worth preserving and should be kept youthful while she is still young enough to enjoy it."

Cartoons of Sir Harold Gillies by Tom Webster
of the Daily Mail, *1924*

It was during this year that Gillies and his family moved into a house in Queen Anne Street, a reflection of his increasing prosperity. Just around the corner, at the junction of Harley Street with Marylebone Road, the tall building that had replaced several late Georgian houses was completed. This was to be The London Clinic, a revolutionary ideal of a private hospital, with consulting rooms and operating theatres and beds contained within one precinct. It was initially financed on its opening in 1930 by thirty-six members of the medical profession, including Gillies, who each contributed £2000. In return for their support they were entitled to the use of all the amenities offered by the organisation. Gillies' consulting address was now 149 Harley Street, the back entrance to the London Clinic. It was with great regret that the eight-year-old partnership of Kilner and Gillies was consequently dissolved. They both decided that with so much work now available it would be to their mutual disadvantage to remain in practice together.

These changes made Gillies' life somewhat easier. He could now operate on his private patients in one efficiently run premises, as opposed to the previous inconveniences of travelling from one nursing home to another, operating under poor conditions and transporting great quantities of instruments from place to place.

Gillies first became associated with Rainsford Mowlem[18] in 1930. Mowlem, a fellow New Zealander, was a general surgeon at the Hammersmith Hospital and in the course of his work there had come into contact with a number of Gillies' patients inspiring a conversion to the cause of

18 Rainsford Mowlem. Qualified Otago, MB, Ch. B., NZ 1924. Surgeon i/c Plastic Dept. Middlesex Hospital / Centre for Plastic Surgery, Mount Vernon, Northwood. Consulting Plastic Surgeon Birmingham Accident Hospital / Luton and Dunstable Hospital / King Edward VII Hospital, Windsor / St Luke's Hospital. Assoc. Surgeon in Plastic Surgery, Prince of Wales General Hospital. Ex-President BAPS.

plastic surgery. This was a significant year for Gillies. He received his highest accolade to date: he was knighted by King George V for his services to his country during the Great War of 1914-1918.

Extract from the London Gazette, July, 1930:

Central Chancery of the Orders of Knighthood,

St. James's Palace, S.W.2.

Tuesday, June 3rd., 1930.

The King has been graciously pleased, on the occasion of His Majesty's Birthday, to signify his intention of conferring the honour of Knighthood on:

Harold Delf Gillies, Esq., C.B.S., F.R.C.S., L.R.C.P., Major R.A.M.C. (retd.), Chief Plastic Surgeon to the Ministry of Pensions. For valuable services in the treatment of facial disfigurement.

page 3474.
Investiture page 3874.

1930 – 1939

Whatsoever a man soweth, that shall he also reap
– St Paul

The year of Gillies' knighthood also saw his election to the post of consulting plastic surgeon to St Bartholomew's Hospital. This must have been a most moving experience for him: here at last was the recognition for which he had struggled so long, recognition not only for himself, but also - of far more significance to him - for plastic surgery. The new science had been officially accepted into the ancient preserves of surgery; of this Sir Harold was proud.

The first years at Barts were by no means easy. Sir Harold was allocated four beds, eventually increased to a total of eight. He was compelled to rely upon the kindness of his colleagues for the accommodation of any extra patients. Thanks to the confidence with which his fellow surgeons regarded him, he was rarely unable to find the additional beds that he needed.

In 1930 Sir Harold's cousin, A.H. Mclndoe, arrived in England from America. Since his emigration from New Zealand, Mclndoe had worked with the Mayo brothers in Rochester. The previous year, Lord Moynihan[19] had

19 Berkley George Andrew Moynihan, 1st Baron Moynihan, 1865 – 1936. Qualified Leeds 1887. Surgeon to Leeds Infirmary 1906. Professor of Clinical Surgery in the University of Leeds 1909. Knighthood 1912. Baronet 1922. Vice Chancellor Leeds University 1924. Appointed con-

visited the Mayo Clinic and remarked upon the promise shown by McIndoe, the young registrar working in gastric surgery. Lord Moynihan told him of the opportunities in England open to good surgeons, and advised McIndoe to move to London and attempt to secure a post with the then expanding Postgraduate Medical School. Without due consideration McIndoe sailed for England, only to find that London was already overcrowded with young surgeons seeking similar jobs. He had had no alternative but to appeal to his cousin, Sir Harold Gillies, for help.

Gillies, who had, in fact, never met McIndoe (and who always insisted he had never heard of him either!), took pity on him and used his influence to find him at least a temporary job. He consulted Sir Philip Manson-Bahr who advised that McIndoe try for the post of lecturer in surgery at The Hospital for Tropical Diseases. Once McIndoe had secured the position, Sir Harold offered him an assistantship within his practice. For a year their relationship was one of chief and assistant, but in 1931, Gillies proposed that McIndoe should join him on a permanent partnership basis, having ascertained that his cousin was indeed a brilliant and imaginative surgeon.

They operated together regularly at Barts, Dollis Hill and at the London Clinic, and the older man taught McIndoe the techniques and methods used in plastic surgery. Gillies gave McIndoe his full support and it helped the unestablished surgeon immensely to have his name

---

sulting surgeon Leeds Infirmary 1926. President of Royal College of Surgeons 1926 – 1932. Raised to peerage as Baron Moynihan of Leeds 1929.

associated with one whose professional status ranked so high. Together they produced papers, the younger man preparing the manuscripts for publication, and the name of McIndoe was for the first time brought before the eyes of the medical profession. There was now a loose partnership of three men, Gillies, Mowlem and McIndoe, operating out of the London Clinic, which was to remain intact until 1939.

In 1932 Sir Harold developed a severe phlebitis of his right foot and was confined to his bed for eight weeks. *The Daily Express*, misconstruing his confinement, published a report intimating that he was in fact on his death bed. The article was suspiciously reminiscent of an obituary and provoked a strong protest from Sir Harold. The paper published an apology the following day with an air of injured innocence.

He did find the illness most aggravating, and to fill the many hours of immobility, took lessons in draughtsmanship and painting. Before his discovery of Professor Tonks in 1916, he had had tuition in sketching but had little time in his full life to pursue this. In the course of his work he had come across many problems concerning facial form and dimension, and had often sought the services of professional artists and sculptors, especially those of F. Derwent Wood, RA, who had helped to solve the problem of aesthetics in the satisfactory construction of facial prostheses. It irked Sir Harold that he did not have the technical knowledge to express his own ideas in graphic form, and he tackled the acquisition of this knowledge most seriously. He found great pleasure in painting and it was evident that he had a decided feeling for composition and colour. He also discovered that many others in the medical profession sought relaxation in painting and he organised the Medical Art Society for their use. The first meeting was held in his club, The Garrick, the same year, the senior member being Sir Leonard Hill, the physiologist. The Society thereafter held annual exhibitions at the Royal Society of Medicine at 1 Wimpole Street.

In 1934 Sir Harold was elected Honorary Fellow of the American College of Surgeons, and whilst in the United States to receive his degree, gave the Charles H. Mayo Lecture with the title, 'The Development and Scope of Plastic Surgery'.

His private practice was by now well-established and Sir Harold could afford to leave much of the work to his assistants and partners. He was finally able to indulge in all the pursuits he loved so well, in golf, in painting and in fishing.

During the years between his knighthood and the Second World War, many celebrities consulted him, among them Leopold, King of the Belgians. In 1934 Sir Harold had removed two impacted wisdom teeth which were thought to be affecting the King's sight. This operation was performed with the utmost secrecy in the Manor Court Nursing Home in Folkestone. In 1935 they met again as a result of the tragic car accident outside Lucerne in which Queen Astrid had been killed. King Leopold had sustained injuries to his face and left arm on that fateful day in August, and, in December, after the wounds had healed, consulted Sir Harold in his rooms at the London Clinic. His scars were excised and all visible evidence of the crash was successfully removed.

Another case which reached the columns of the daily press was that of the small boy in the Royal Infirmary, Stoke-on-Trent, who had lost an ear. Sir Harold removed the corresponding ear from the boy's grandmother and grafted it on to the tissue around the exposed external auditory meatus. This transposition was highly successful but not as miraculous as the press would have wished their readers to believe. Sir Harold had, in fact, completed considerable research into the use of maternal cartilage for the reconstruction of the auricle, and subsequently published his findings in 1937.

Sir Harold was undoubtedly the surgeon favoured by high society. He was consulted by numerous luminaries and socialites for the repair of injuries sustained in car crashes and hunting accidents. The newspapers were only too anxious to report such cases as that of Daisy Kennedy, the violinist wife of John Drinkwater, whose scars Sir Harold had removed at the St Mary Abbott's Hospital in March, 1937.

Despite the demands of his fast-growing private practice, Sir Harold managed to publish original papers with regularity. In 1938 he produced a paper on the reconstruction of the syphilitic nose, a problem which had held his interest since 1923. It was to speak on this subject that Professor Sauerbruch invited him to a meeting of the Medical Society of Berlin.

Sir Harold had observed with distaste the rising tide of Nazism and had firsthand knowledge of Hitler's professional purges from German colleagues who had taken refuge in England. It was one of these colleagues who translated into German the address which he was to give in Berlin. This was recorded on to gramophone discs at the Blind School in Regent's Park and synchronised to the proposed order of the slides that were to be shown. Sir Harold hoped sincerely that the voice of the exiled German would be recognised.

However, with the aid of Siemens, the electrical engineers, the address was uneventful. The account of the

reconstruction of the syphilitic nose and a brief adden-
dum denouncing unqualified beauty surgeons, delivered
by the recorded voice of his German friend and mimed by
Sir Harold, was heard by the audience in an atmosphere of
quiet concentration. At the dinner in his honour after the
meeting, Sir Harold was presented with a bronze bust of
Virchow, for which he produced one of the few German
words that he knew, *"Danke"*.

The last paper he produced before war was declared
concerned techniques in mammaplasty. Morestin, as early
as 1915, had described methods for the reduction of breast
tissue by operative means and Sir Harold had discussed
briefly the problems of breast surgery in *Plastic Surgery
of the Face* in 1920. But in many quarters this new paper
met with a bad reception; "When I first began to undertake breast reductions I was almost burned at the stake,"
he said. The dictum 'What God hath given, let no man
take away' was obviously widely misapplied. Gillies and
McIndoe tersely defended their techniques with the words,
"Today there is little need to justify plastic surgical procedures on the pendulous breast. It is a field as genuine as any
other in reconstructive surgery provided its limitations are
recognised and the cases are carefully selected."

Sir Harold at a Cambridge graduates dinner
By kind permission of Barrats Photo Press Ltd.

1939 – 1945

Silence is the soul of war; deliberate counsel must prepare
The mighty work which valour must complete –
Matthew Prior

At last, the almost unbearable tension that had built up since the Munich crisis was broken. Poland was invaded by the Nazis and Britain and France declared war upon Germany.

In 1938 the War Office had laid plans for the deployment of the medical services in the event of hostilities breaking out that year or in the near future. Sir Harold, in his capacity as Consultant Plastic Surgeon to the Army at Home and the Ministry of Health, had been asked to develop proposals for the expansion and organisation of the plastic surgery service in case of a national emergency.

With the fear of immediate attack from the air, all units were to be evacuated from London and dispersed throughout the Home Counties to safe but accessible hospitals. Sir Harold had selected possible sites for the units and the surgeons who were to lead them were permitted to inspect their prospective establishments. Mclndoe, with great foresight, had chosen the Queen Victoria Hospital in East Grinstead, and it was to this small hospital that he and Jayes moved on the declaration of war. Kilner stayed with his Ministry of Pensions Unit at Roehampton, while Mowlem and Barron travelled to St Albans. Sir Harold had chosen for himself the Park Prewett Hospital, a former mental home outside Basingstoke. Within the grounds of the hospital stood Rooksdown House which had previously been the private block, and it was in this building that he established himself and his unit. The lounge was converted into operating theatres and the separate rooms into wards.

The staff at Rooksdown House was comprised of a chief assistant, James Cuthbert[20], a former registrar at Barts; a dental surgeon, Martin Rushton; an anaesthetist, Patrick Shackleton; and a newly qualified nurse, Dorothy Whiteside, as Matron.

For the first months of the war Sir Harold was rarely at Rooksdown. The casualties as yet were few and there was still much work to be done by him in London in policy making and organising new plastic surgery units in Birmingham, Liverpool, Manchester and Leeds. In addition to creating these units, Sir Harold instilled new life into existing establishments and oversaw the expansion of those in Newcastle, Stoke-on-Trent and Gloucester. This labour was achieved with the aid of Sir William Kelsey Fry.

By the time the first great influx of casualties arrived during the withdrawal from Dunkirk, there was an efficient and fully-staffed organisation prepared to give immediate treatment: a very different situation compared to the availability of plastic surgery in the First World War. A unit had

20 J. B. Cuthbert, FRCS. Qualified SBH, 1937. Plastic Surgeon i/c Johannesburg Hospital.

been sent with the British Expeditionary Force to France under Richard Battle, a surgeon trained by Sir Harold. This was the first of the Army plastic surgery units that were to travel with and operate behind the line of battle.

The idea of mobile plastic surgery units was conceived by Sir Harold, who had been so thankful to receive well-dressed and healed wounds from Kazanjian's Jaw Unit in France during the First World War. But these units were not to be mere primary dressing stations; they were to act as self-sufficient and independent entities, treating and repairing as many soldiers as possible without reference to hospitals in England.

Unit No. 1 was rescued from the beaches of Dunkirk and was later redeployed during the North African campaign at Alexandria. Unit No. 2 under Oldfield was sent to work in Cairo to help with the influx of casualties from the bitter fighting in the desert.

Unit No. 3 under Heanley travelled to India to receive casualties from the Burma front and was later joined by a unit organised by the Indian Army Medical Corps.

At the start of the war there were only six full-time plastic surgeons and the pressing urgency for more specialists in this field was a great problem. Rooksdown House was the main training centre for the leaders of the units, but the training of a plastic surgeon was necessarily an extended process, and there was a relatively long period of inefficiency whilst the team that made up the unit settled down in active service. Sir Harold appealed to the War Office to allow each group of personnel to train together. The idea met with approval and the first team to be produced as such, Unit No. 4, was sent to Africa to accept casualties from Tunisia in 1942, and eventually moved, with Unit No. 1, to the theatre of war in Italy.

Eventually, Units No. 5 and No. 6 were to land on the beaches of Normandy, and Sir Harold visited them in Holland before they crossed in the wake of the main thrust across the Rhine in 1945. By the end of the war each unit had treated an average of 3000 patients, of which only 18% of face and jaw cases and 20% of burns cases were sent back to Rooksdown. Sir Harold kept in touch with the leaders of each unit by letter. Problems were discussed, new procedures explained, and morale was kept high by cheerful anecdotes of wartime England.

Casualties sent to England were labelled by the units abroad and either flown to RAF Wroughton and hence by ambulance to Rooksdown, or were transported to Rooksdown's own station by train. Here, a great variety of cases were received from both the Services and the civilian population, unlike the unit at East Grinstead which specialised almost exclusively in airmen's burns.

In 1941 America remained uncommitted in the European struggle, and was observing with anxiety the uncomfortable stalemate between England and the all-conquering Germany. In October, the American Government invited Sir Harold to visit the United States to lecture on plastic work and the British war effort. Sir Harold spoke in Chicago and then spent some weeks touring South America. On his return to North America in December he attended a luncheon given in his honour by the American Association of Oral and Plastic Surgeons. He met again his colleagues of the First World War days, many of whom he had not seen since 1919. Here to pay homage to their old master were Ferris Smith, John Straige Davies, Fulton Risdon, G. M. Dorrance, Vilray P. Blair and Robert H. Ivy. It must have been most gratifying to Sir Harold to know he had retained the friendship and loyalty of so many of his fellow surgeons.

Sir Harold returned to England in the bomb bay of a Liberator aircraft of the USAF in time for a Christmas fraught with the anxieties of the pending German invasion.

Meanwhile, the battle in the air had developed, and burned airmen were filling the plastic surgery units in England. East Grinstead took the brunt of this work, but Rooksdown also received many of the casualties. It was one of these pilots who introduced into Rooksdown the A-12 strain of haemolytic streptococcus.

McIndoe had already experienced the devastating effects of the haemolytic streptococcus. The germ destroyed within hours the vulnerable tubed pedicles which melted away like snow in the sun, wasting many hours of work and much valuable tissue. It was for this reason that McIndoe decided to adopt the less susceptible free skin graft for the repair of burns.

Sir Harold asked Colonel L. Colebrook[21], Director of Pathology for the Army at Home, to visit Rooksdown and devise some method of eliminating the germ. Colonel Colebrook typed the streptococcus and enforced rigorous aseptic discipline in the unit. Special dressing rooms were set aside in which non-touch technique was used by

21 Leonard Colebrook, FRS, FRCS, FRCOG (Retired). Qualified St Mary's 1906. Late Hon. Director, Research Laboratories Queen Charlotte's Hospital/Medical Research Council Burns Unit Birmingham Accident Hospital.

gowned and masked nurses; sulfonamides were used to quell the infections as they broke out; no wound dressings were allowed to take place until fully two hours had elapsed after bed-making and sweeping. After a prolonged battle it seemed as though the streptococcus had been eradicated. A celebration was held to mark the occasion and Colebrook was congratulated on his achievement. However, it was only a few weeks later that the A-12 haemolytic streptococcus re-established itself, this time resistant to sulfonamides. The germ continued to plague the unit until its final extinction on the introduction of penicillin.

The atmosphere at Rooksdown was one of informality and tolerance, and there existed an absolute trust in the relationship between the surgeons and their patients. These factors contributed greatly towards the high morale of the unit. Not only were the operations a success, the recovery of the patients was rapid in their happy environment.

Sir Harold had given much thought to the pre-operative nursing methods used in the cases of serious injuries to the face and neck. In these patients there were great risks of respiratory obstruction due to debris and blood and the sequel of lung damage and infection. As much use as possible, therefore, was made of early suction, expectorants, postural drainage and physiotherapy. The recovery of a casualty was as much due to this careful nursing as to the skill of the surgeon who would have been powerless without its aid.

In 1941 the free Danes living in England presented Sir Harold with the sum of £3000 to build a badly needed recreation pavilion for Rooksdown. The money was offered with the thanks of the Danish people for the work which

Sir Harold had performed after the *Geysir* disaster in 1924. In January of the same year the Queen Alexandra Pavilion was opened by Lady Louis Mountbatten in the presence of the Countess of Malmesbury, the Danish Ambassador and the subscribers to the fund. The pavilion stands today and sees much use as weekly dances are held in it for the patients and staff of Rooksdown where, according to Sir Harold, "it is common to see a surgical student dancing with a forehead flap and nurses waltzing with tubed pedicles." The pavilion also acted as the headquarters of the Red Cross during the war.

Between 1944 and 1946, Sir Harold built up the Rooksdown Club, an exact parallel of McIndoe's notorious Guinea Pig Club. It had its first meeting in 1947 and eventually grew to a thousand members. It was registered under the War Charities Act and played a large part in the rehabilitation of the more seriously disabled of Rooksdown's previous patients.

After D-day, Queen Wilhelmina and Princess Juliana of the Netherlands paid Rooksdown an informal visit, since the unit contained many Dutch among its cosmopolitan inmates. The Royals were most moved and impressed by the work at the unit, work which is carried on to this day: Rooksdown is a lasting testimony to the pride and affection with which Sir Harold Gillies regarded the art of plastic surgery in the relief of suffering humanity.

Sir Harold on the occasion of his 70th birthday

By courtesy of the Universal Pictorial Agency

1945 − 1960

Sleep after toyle, port after stormie seas,
Ease after warre, death after life, does greatly please

− Spenser

After the war, Marshal Tito had appealed to the UNRRA (United Nations Relief and Rehabilitation Administration) for help in the repair of the many mutilated invalids from his armed forces. Sir Harold was asked to visit Yugoslavia to determine the extent of the aid which would be required.

He perceived that the Communist authorities' only interest was in a British team performing the entire work: this would have been impossible as there was sufficient reconstructive surgery in England alone to occupy the time of all plastic units for many months to come. Sir Harold explained the situation, and on behalf of the UNRRA, offered to arrange for a plastic surgery unit to visit Yugoslavia on the understanding that it would instruct Communist surgeons in technique and method with a view to the foundation of a permanent civilian service.

This arrangement did not appeal to the Yugoslavian government at all, but after much hesitation, it was accepted. Sir Harold returned to England, and James Cuthbert, Rushton the dental surgeon, Shackleton the anaesthetist and matron Whiteside, were dispatched to Yugoslavia. The unit worked for many months with various changes of staff. Sir Harold later commented, "This friendly gesture, at a time when Yugoslavia was far from happy, may have had a small part in her drift towards the West."

When Sir Harold next ventured behind the Iron Curtain on a lecture tour in 1948, Marshal Tito invited him to his home. Tito had, it transpired, attended Sir Harold's lecture in Belgrade in 1945 on his first visit to Yugoslavia. "While proudly displaying his private fruit grove," Sir Harold remembers, "he plucked a lemon and presented it to me. Whereupon he was requested to sign the fruit; this was the Order of the Lemon, First Class."

In 1946 Sir Harold was one of the instigators of the formation of the British Association of Plastic Surgeons. The aims of the organisation were to propagate the art and science of plastic surgery within the framework of surgery itself, and to stimulate understanding and cooperation between plastic surgeons and the medical profession and public. Sir Harold was honoured by being the Association's first president.

The problem of the relationship of the plastic surgeons with the profession and the public was, and still is, very great. There is an inherent distrust, indeed a strong prejudice, in many of the older members of the profession which leads them to believe that plastic surgery is both unethical and unnecessary. As a result, many unhappy and deserving patients are denied the services which plastic surgery can give to them. Today the Association is powerful, and it is able to defend its members in any action bought against them by the General Medical Council or in a court of law.

It may be remembered that in the 1960s several distinguished plastic surgeons were accused by the GMC of advertising in the public press. Through the able and successful
defence put forward by the Association on behalf of its
members, weight was added to the appeal for the mod-
ernisation of Clause 5B of the General Medical Council
regulations. Sir Harold's particular part in this appeal will
be discussed later.

1948 saw the institution of the National Health Service.
Sir Harold had played a major part, in his capacity of consultant to the Ministry of Health, in determining the role
plastic surgery was to take in the Welfare State, and it is
mainly due to him that plastic surgery today is fully inte-
grated into the functioning of the service.

Rooksdown had been, during the war, of a truly cosmopolitan nature and many foreign plastic surgeons had
been trained by Sir Harold during that period. It was for
his work in the training of Norwegian surgeons that he
was created, in 1948, Commander of the Order of St Olav.

Since 1916, Sir Harold had been much concerned with
medical photography, and, in conjunction with Kodak, was
responsible for the first colour film of a plastic operation
to be taken. In recognition of this, he was invited in 1950
to become Chairman of the Medical Group of the Royal
Photographic Society, in succession to Sir Cecil Wakeley.
Sir Harold took great interest in the proceedings of the
Society, never failing to attend the monthly meetings, and
was elected Fellow of the Royal Photographic Society in
1952.

In 1951, while still holding office within the Royal Photographic Society, he showed publicly for the first time his

paintings of Iceland as part of a chairman's address entitled 'Surgery, Sagas and Salmon'. He had visited Iceland for the first time in 1950 and the country was to become just as much as inspiration for his painting as Scotland.

In 1952 his work appeared for the second time in the Royal Institute of Oil Painters' annual exhibition. He had made his debut at the exhibition in 1940 when his depictions of the peaceful river Test made a sad contrast with the bomb-blasted galleries. In 1952 his contributions were all of an Icelandic theme.

Painting, in fact, was now his main pastime, and wherever he travelled in the course of his work he was accompanied by his paints and canvases. His regular visits to the Strathcaro Hospital near Edinburgh always marked an opportunity to paint, as well as to fish the famed salmon beat at Shotley Bridge.

At the age of seventy it was with great regret that he had to retire from Rooksdown. Although he had found the long operating sessions with the unit too much for his failing health (he had for some years been suffering from arteriosclerosis), he still undertook private work and consulted regularly at the London Clinic.

Sir Harold now had the leisure to concentrate on a task which had occupied his mind for some time: the writing of a work on the development of plastic surgery. He had always taken great pains to keep an accurate record of all cases that passed through his hands, and had aggregated over the years a unique collection of photographs illustrating not only the immediate results of his operations, but also the mature appearance of the grafts and implants.

In conjunction with Ralph Millard[22], who had been his pupil in 1948, he assembled a mass of informative and illustrative material. All that remained was its arrangement for publication, and for this Sir Harold planned an entirely novel approach to the presentation of a textbook.

His conception, which indeed suits the crystalisation of a life's work, was that of autobiographical informality. The text was to be eminently readable, with the photographs and illustrations appearing unnumbered beside the appropriate descriptive print. This was Sir Harold's, and indeed all students', ideal of a good textbook – not a mere volume of reference but rather a book which would make light work of the acquisition and assimilation of knowledge.

Several publishers in England were approached. From most came polite refusals to handle the work. Others were more shocked by the subject matter and the graphic images, indeed one firm complained bitterly that the appearance of such a book would either irreparably damage the reputation of its publishers, or that of British surgery. Sir Harold began to despair of ever finding a sponsor, until finally, in 1956, Little, Brown and Company of Boston USA accepted the responsibility.

Two years of work were involved in setting up the material for printing. His editor at Little, Brown, Theodore Phillips, tells of the arrival of the manuscript, part handwritten, part typed, with 3,500 photographs in three oddly shaped suitcases which he later discovered were from the

22 D Ralph Millard, Jr., MD Diplomate, American Board of Plastic Surgery; Assistant Clinical Professor, University of Miami School of Medicine; Consultant in Plastic Surgery to St Joseph's Hospital, Asheville, North Carolina / United States Navel Hospital, Key West, Florida.

boot of Sir Harold's Bentley, which had been sold to cover initial costs.

The Principles and Art of Plastic Surgery gradually took shape while caustic letters from Sir Harold expressing disapproval of the editor's work regularly crossed the Atlantic. The book was finally published in May 1957 and met with enthusiastic approval from its critics, especially in America. Its appearance was exactly as Sir Harold had envisaged: two volumes laid out in a form which would engage the attention of the reader at all times. *The Principles and Art of Plastic Surgery* was the history of the speciality written by its instigator and greatest exponent, a book with a unique place in the history of surgery.

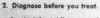

2. Diagnose before you treat.

A principle vividly expounded in the medical wards of Bart's.

'Just by a tiny Kentish cottage there ran a little stream which always held good trout in May-fly season. There was one fish who would never let us get within twenty yards of him before he submerged and refused to rise. On closer observation I made the *diagnosis*. There was a moor-hen's nest not a yard below this fish's usual rise and it was the moor-hen's fluttering off her nest that was tipping the wink to the fish that fishermen were about. I enjoyed moor-hen's eggs for lunch and the fish for supper.

An extract from The Principles and Art of Plastic Surgery
with a sketch by Sir Harold Gillies

In 1955, the first meeting of the International Society of Plastic Surgeons was held. There gathered in Stockholm surgeons from all the world over, many of whom had been Sir Harold's pupils and all of whom owed him their gratitude for the foundation of their speciality. They expressed their thanks by unanimously electing him their first president, and gratified him further by electing many of his protégés to posts on the executive committee, including Sir Archibald McIndoe and Dr Ralph Millard.

The visit to Sweden was followed by an invitation from the Government of New Zealand to give a series of lectures in Australasia. This was to be the first time Sir Harold had visited his homeland since 1904, his second year at Cambridge.

Sir Harold and Lady Gillies determined that they should take this opportunity to visit three members of their family, who, on marrying, had left England. They first flew to Nairobi where one of their two daughters lived, and then travelled further into Africa to see their youngest son, an entomologist working on the problems of disease transport in Tanganyika. From here they made their way to New Zealand where their eldest son was now settled.

The visits and travelling occupied four months. Before his return to England, Sir Harold was invited to read a paper to the Royal College of Surgeons in Sydney where he was elected to an Honorary Fellowship of the College.

In March 1957, Sir Harold exhibited his paintings with the United Society of Artists at the RBA Galleries. The catalogue had unfortunately been misprinted and Sir Harold was introduced as, "Sir Harold Gittins, the plastic surgeon, whose sure and steady hand employs pigments in a brush-mark-less technique that produces a silky finish." This annoyed intensely the art critic of the *Star*, who, having demolished Sir Harold's picture, 'Sunrise Loch Boisdale', (35 gns) with few but damning words, went on to comment, "The adulatory attitude towards the pictures of amateurs distinguished in fields other than painting is ridiculous when it comes from an allegedly serious society of painters...Sir Harold's pictures...are frankly bad."

However, two years later, in June 1959, a most successful exhibition of his work was held in Foyles Art Gallery. Many of his paintings were sold, at an average price of £21, to colleagues and collectors. In fact, there was a minor scandal when J. Paul Getty attempted to buy 'Calm Fjord, Laerdal', a picture which was lent for the occasion by a friend. Mr Getty did not see any other picture which pleased him and he left soon after.

Sir Harold Gillies with Christina Foyle and Lord Portal of Hungerford at the Foyles Galleries Exhibition.

By kind permission of Thomson Newspapers Ltd.

In May 1957 Sir Harold's wife Elizabeth died. Four months later he remarried. His second wife was Miss Marjorie E. Clayton, who had been his surgical assistant since 1937. That November he travelled to India on the invitation of the Government to operate and lecture. He was away from England for ten weeks.

While still in India, the *Sunday Times* published an article under his name entitled 'Sex and Psyche'. This was a discussion of the problems occurring in the treatment of humans of indistinct gender, a controversial topic much in the public eye due to the recent case of Robert/Roberta Cowell. Sir Harold, who had not, in fact, been involved on this particular occasion, had had experiences of a similar nature[23] and was well qualified to write upon the subject.

The article was of no particular intrinsic importance but was the precursor of the chain of events which led to the writing of the letter entitled 'The Price of Ethics', published in the *British Medical Journal* in April 1959.

In 1948 Sir Harold's cousin, Sir Archibald McIndoe, had been elected Councillor of the Royal College of Surgeons and was voted to the position of Vice-President in 1957. The college, after ten years of State medicine, was in dire financial straits, and £3m had to be raised to meet the costs of maintenance and planned expansion. Sir Simon Marks, who had been a generous benefactor of medical research and learning, advised Sir Archibald to launch a public appeal. The College Appeal Committee was chaired by Lord Kindersley; the vice-chairman was Sir Simon Marks himself. It was decided that publicity for the appeal should

23 *Vide*: 'Works'.

be obtained through the media of newspapers and television. Press conferences were held and the nature of the appeal was explained.

The weeks that followed culminated in the following leader in the *British Medical Journal* editorial of April 25th, 1959:

A photograph in a Sunday newspaper a few weeks ago showed the President and the Council of the Royal College of Surgeons of England (and others) listening to the Hunterian Oration. Leaning forward earnestly from a solitary column of type was the orator himself. The names of those in the two front rows were given in full so the reader should be in no doubt as to their identity. Not long after this, gossip-column writers described with glee a party in Lincoln's Inn Fields where stars of the *Emergency Ward 10* film drank cocktails with the College's famous skeletons. Photographs again. As the President of the College of Surgeons is the most unassuming and modest of men, it was obvious there must be something desperately wrong with the present state of the College for him to assent to this kind of publicity. Like many a private doctor suspected of advertising, it wanted, and wants, money - and apparently quite a lot. The College deserves it. It is a national institution built up by the labours of famous men. But many national appeals for money have been launched before this without attempts to publicize the persons behind the cause of the appeal. The College of Surgeons could probably raise the money it wants without losing its dignity and without giving publicity to the members of its council. No one could have felt at all happy at seeing the full-page advertisement in last week's *New Statesman* and *Spectator* announcing the presentation by Granada on ITV of SUR-GEON - printing the names of the President and six members of the College Council (two of them also members of the BMA Council), complete with degrees, diplomas, orders, and honours. And then, last Sunday, a picture in a Sunday newspaper of a rather perplexed PRCS rehearsing for this Thursday's show.

This Journal has a great respect for the present President of the Royal College of Surgeons of England. No one who knows him can doubt that his first concern is for his college and the last is for himself. He is not in private practice, and therefore does not stand to gain any professional advantage from the present series of publicity stunts of which he is the unwitting centrepiece. Doubtless they are as distasteful to him as they may be pleasing to the ingenious minds which have thought them up. We hope the College will raise the money it needs. We hope, too, that the President will look a bit more critically at the advice he is receiving from the promoters of the various schemes for raising it. It would be a pity if the College, in achieving its target of £3m, it found that in the process it had lost something more precious than money.

Official disapproval of the publicity campaign (and the thinly veiled hint that it was thought that certain Fellows of the College were advertising) unnerved many of its backers, not the least Sir Archibald McIndoe, who had been its chief sponsor. Sir Harold was incensed by this attack on the College and on McIndoe in particular, and wrote the following letter to the *British Medical Journal* (June 13th 1959):

The Price of Ethics

Sir, - How anyone can complain of the ethics of that wonderful photograph of the College Council passes comprehension ('Top Surgeons', Journal, April 25, p. 1100). X's only complaint is that X wasn't a good enough surgeon to be included. After all, we voted them there, and good cess to them.

At 76 + I hope there are still a few friends who will credit me with a life that has been devoted to surgery, and to a particular branch - the surgery of the maimed, the wounded, and the burned. It is unfair but inevitable that through the thrust of the press the limelight should be thrown on such subjects as hole in the heart, insulin, penicillin, psychiatry, or even plastic surgery. Having had a hand in developing the present plastic surgery service of our country, of which the Health Service may well be proud, I can speak with feeling of the encouragement given to this young subject in the 1920s, not only by the great medical journals but also by such dedicated individuals as Lord Northcliffe, Beaverbrook, Owen Seaman, Squire Sprigge, and, later, Lord Nuffield. Their press, their approval helped on the work, educated the public and obtained facilities necessary to its progress to the benefit of many disfigured folk and to the credit of British surgery.

Some body outside the profession has got to put it across, some body or bodies inside the profession have to be utilized, even against their interests, to further these aims by explanation and interview. One small note in the press may influence in a few days the trend of medical treatment which otherwise might take years to percolate. Far quicker and more potent is the television technique. It educates the public in the truths of our lovely profession, and what harm if one or two men get a tiny puff? Cannot we be tolerant as well as clever and ethical? Unfortunately Mr A, who is written up by some thrustful journalist, may be one of our worst qualified and shadiest of practitioners, while Dr B, with less glamour and more ability, stays hidden under his bushel of ethical modesty. Is not the answer to be found in educating the press to our standards?

I wonder whose pocket and whose dignity suffers from such an excellent television programme as that recent one depicting an operation for hare-lip. It could hardly have been more sympathetically shown, and must have given a great deal of comfort to parents and of instruction to their medical practitioners. There seems to be a false idea that as a result of such publicity all the hare-lip babies in Britain would immediately be rushed off to the operator televised. My own experience of this type of publicity is that only a few rather hopeless individuals seek an appointment without a doctor's reference and impecunious to boot. As a form of successful advertising it is therefore a wash-out. But as a means of spreading among the populace, including the medical profession, the great advances in British medicine and surgery, publicity properly controlled should be welcomed with an open heart.

I think it is magnificent that the president of the Royal College of Surgeons and his councillors and counsellors should devote so much time and energy to raise money for the good of surgery and not for their own gain. These men have all deserved great credit for the unselfish work they have done, and is it not preposterous that they should be called to account by a vociferous group of people who appear to enjoy criticizing the ethics of others? Are not the Peter Mays and the Denis Comptons of our profession better than the press critics?

On a Sunday soon and for the following five Sundays The Sunday 'X', ambitious to capture the doctors as readers, had proposed to publish my life-story written by myself about golf and fishing, and all sorts of things I've enjoyed with my medical pals, and of course my efforts at surgery. These articles would have been quite harmless, the offer prodigious - £6,500. On advice and after much brain-washing, I have wistfully turned it down. Am I right, or a fool? Could the GMC be persuaded to modernize Clause 5b? - I am, etc.,

HAROLD GILLIES
London, W1

This helped to encourage the members of the Appeal Committee, and no more than a year passed before the sum of £2m had been raised towards the fund. The remaining money, however, was obtained in a more discreet manner.

The last trip abroad that Sir Harold was to undertake took place in August 1959 when he was invited by the Colombian government to visit South America to lecture and to receive an honorary degree.

Sir Harold and Lady Gillies flew to Bogota, the capital of Colombia, where he spent some weeks sightseeing and painting between his various commitments. He was especially enchanted by the Gold Museum, a complex of vaults containing many of the treasured heirlooms from past civilisations of South America. On his return to England he retired from private practice to his home at Church Oakley near the town of Basingstoke.

The last occasion upon which the public was to hear of him was during the July of 1960. Geoffrey Griffin, the South African fast bowler, had been continuously accused by umpires of throwing during the Test Match Series. Griffin's arm was, in fact, bent due to bad setting of the humerus after fracture. Sir Harold had suffered himself from a similar accident when he had been playing golf for England, and had designed an aluminium splint to keep his left arm straight whilst driving. Upon hearing of Griffin's plight he collected his splint from Edward Holdright's golfing school in Regent's Park and took it to Lord's where the South African Test team were playing. Griffin used the splint in the nets and during several County matches, but never, unfortunately, during the Tests themselves.

After a short illness, the result of his arteriosclerosis, Sir Harold Gillies died at the London Clinic on September 10th 1960, at the age of seventy-eight.

He left assets totalling £20,179, and he willed that each of his four children should receive £250 and that the residue should become the property of Lady Marjorie Gillies. The revenue from the royalties and the sale of copyrights was to be equally divided between his family.

Epilogue

His life was gentle; and the elements so mixed in him, that nature
might stand up and say to all the world, 'This was a man'
         – William Shakespeare

In 1961 the British Association of Plastic Surgeons inaugurated The Gillies Memorial Lecture. The money with which the lectureship was endowed was also to provide grants to foster education, study and research in plastic surgery.

Earlier that spring, The American Society of Plastic and Reconstructive Surgery had invited Sir Harold to receive their Special Honorary Citation in recognition of his work in the advancement of plastic surgery. The presentation was to take place at the President's Banquet during the 29th Annual Meeting of the Society on October 6th 1960 in Los Angeles, California. Sir Harold had accepted this invitation in a letter to Dr Kenneth Pickrell. After his death Lady Gillies wrote to Dr Pickrell,

> "...I am certain that it would be Sir Harold's wish that nothing should be altered or changed at the meeting and that it should proceed as if we both were there. Please offer my sincere thanks to all of the members of the American Society of Plastic and Reconstructive Surgery.
> Yours sincerely, Marjorie Clayton (Sam)"
> September 27th 1960

Mr Patrick Clarkson, Sir Harold's pupil and protégé, travelled to America to receive the Citation on behalf of Lady Gillies. It read:

SPECIAL HONORARY CITATION TO SIR
HAROLD GILLIES IN RECOGNITION OF HIS
DEVELOPMENT OF THE SPECIALITY OF
PLASTIC SURGERY, AND HIS OUTSTANDING
SCIENTIFIC CONTRIBUTIONS TO THE
ADVANCEMENT OF ITS PRACTICE. PRESENTED
BY THE AMERICAN SOCIETY OF PLASTIC AND
RECONSTRUCTIVE SURGERY OCTOBER 6, 1960,
LOS ANGELES, CALIFORNIA.

During the Meeting itself Dr Jerome Webster paid tribute to Sir Harold Gillies in the reading of a memorial paper. He concluded his tribute with the words, "Gillies' name might perish, but his influence will be immortal."

Obituaries appeared for many weeks in the public and medical press of England and America. The contributors, personal friends and colleagues of Sir Harold, all found the task of describing his sporting and professional achievements an easy one, but many had great difficulty in capturing the character, the essential moving spirit, of this mercurial genius.

All agreed that Sir Harold had achieved an incredible amount in the short span of a human life, but none quite captured his true nature, except, perhaps, Mr Rainsford Mowlem, who wrote, "[Sir Harold] had a restless, imaginative and ingenious mind which was completely untrammelled by any preconceived ideas as to how things 'should be done.'"

A sporting correspondent, on meeting Sir Harold in 1933, had remarked, "He never takes the most ordinary things of life for granted and is always wondering how they can be improved." It was this combination of imagination, ingenuity and restlessness combined with boundless curiosity and energy that gave Sir Harold his extraordinary success. He had a strength of mind and body which enabled him to pursue his interests and address his duties with a zeal that would have defeated a lesser man.

He had never allowed himself to be weighed down by responsibility, and managed to retain a sense of humour even during the most difficult periods of his life. He was renowned as a practical joker and his colleagues could never foretell in what direction his puckish sense of the ridiculous would find vent. Probably the most famous story is that of 'Dr Scroggie'. On this occasion he refused an invitation to spend a golfing holiday with a group of colleagues, but told his hosts that a Dr Scroggie, a South African, would be taking his place. He disguised himself behind a luxuriant grey beard, donned knickerbockers and cap, and arrived at Westward Ho to join the party. None of his friends recognised him and they spent a most uncomfortable first day debating whether this odd character was indeed Dr Scroggie. At dinner that night, one of the company took the bull by the horns and approached the solitary figure sitting at an isolated table. Sir Harold's plan was to get into the game the next day with a handicap of six and 'clean the house', but, alas he was recognised before he had the chance. His mannerism of holding his cigarette between his second and third finger had given him away.

Many people never quite forgave him for his often misplaced and mistimed jokes at their expense. One of these in particular was Sir Archibald McIndoe, who was unmercifully ragged during the first year with his cousin. One of his favourite tricks was to describe a most complicated operation to a distinguished audience of visiting surgeons, and then to turn to a most inexperienced assistant with a benign smile and say, "Will you cut the graft that I have just been describing, please?"

Despite this disregard for the feelings of others, he was well-loved by his close acquaintances, who understood the quirks of his nature. Dr Rainsford Mowlem said, "He was capable of evoking an enormous though sometimes unwilling affection in all those who knew him well."

Towards the end of his life he gave free rein to his bizarre wit, and was dubbed eccentric by many. He frequently jeopardised his reputation and embarrassed his friends with his sallies. On the occasion that he made public speeches he would always include risqué and irreverent tales, irrespective of the gravity of the function. No doubt he revelled in the sight of the red faces in the audience. Whatever criticism one might level at Sir Harold, nobody could accuse him of being pompous or arch.

His frankness, although an admirable trait, often discredited him in the eyes of those who were the butt of his criticism. However, this characteristic, qualified by a streak of deep humility, would just as often act in his favour; combined with his infectious enthusiasm, it was this that had impressed his superiors in the early days of his career.

He was always sensitive to any deep hurt that he may have inflicted and was in the habit of apologising for his rudeness. He frequently expressed surprise that he had any friends at all and was particularly amazed by the request of the Danish Government to treat the injured from the *Geysir*. The Danish representative that had watched him operate at Sidcup the year before had had particularly large feet and Sir Harold, noticing this, had passed ostentatious remarks about their generous size. Despite the fact everybody agreed that his rudeness was unforgivable, he was always forgiven.

One person who was anathema to him was the fool; he could not tolerate presumption or ignorance, and those unfortunates suffered the cruellest form of his wit. He did, however, freely forgive mistakes made through inexperience, and would always have a kindly word of advice for those who brought their troubles to him.

Many facets of his character were paradoxical. His generosity was well known and many of his pupils, on entering private practice, were financed by Sir Harold. On the other hand he would just as readily refuse some small request for aid with the excuse that he could not afford it. People, in fact, accused him of being 'pound foolish; penny wise'.

He never allowed his patients to discuss the question of fees with him and would always refer them to 'my secretary, Mr Seymour'. Mr Seymour would tell the patient after consultation the fixed fee that Sir Harold charged for their particular operation, and any question of a reduction would be fully discussed and Sir Harold eventually informed of the financial position of his patient. There were many occasions on which patients were treated in return for a nominal fee, or even entirely free.

Unlike his cousin, Sir Archibald McIndoe, Sir Harold did not normally ask exorbitant fees. Due to the time-consuming nature of all plastic operations, fees are necessarily substantial, but nobody could call Sir Harold's charge of £150 for rhinoplasty grossly excessive, for the patient would undergo three or even four operations over periods of months before the new nose passed muster.

The approach to a new private patient played an important part in the eventual psychological, if not physical, result of treatment. Sir Harold advised, "When a patient comes for the first consultation, put him at ease – a cigarette is offered and a bit of polite fencing usually gives an opening. Of course the family doctor may have told or written you about the case already. If not, it may be amusing to conjecture on your own what the patient needs, but let him approach and unfold his reason for coming in his own way; do not interrupt the story. Avoid breaking into the conversation with, 'And what would you like me to do to that huge nose, Sir?' just as he is about to show you his Dupuytren's.

"Once it has been made clear that the patient desires a nasal reduction, no matter how many chins she has, refrain from the temptation to lift her face with your fingers while you are discussing her nasal problem. As soon as the patient's wish has been divulged, try to ascertain the reasons for the desired change. This is important in helping to determine the justifiability of the surgery. If the patient frankly admits, 'Vanity', I am pleased to tell them, 'You could not have a better reason. There is a responsibility in this tricky operation, and if you are not going to be vain about the nose I'm going to give you then I have no interest in doing it.'"

Sir Harold took immense pride in his work and would allow no patient to leave his care until he was perfectly satisfied with the results of the operations. He would never permit his inherent enthusiasm to overcome his better judgment. Each operation was treated as a new problem deserving original thought and action. Before tissues were disturbed, the details of the method to be used were worked out at length and exhaustively. Photographs and plaster casts, in the case of a facial operation, were the maps upon which the campaign was planned. Exact patterns of the skin areas to be grafted were cut from linen and the precise dimensions of the tubed pedicles to be raised were evaluated. This information was draughted carefully on to the skin of the patient before the operation started, with a pen and Bonney's Blue.

As an operator, Sir Harold showed great artistry. That is not to say that his technique was florid or mannered. His every movement was deft and controlled, and his handling of tissues was supremely gentle.

His assistants often found him exasperating to work with. Time would lose all meaning during an operation and his only thought would be for a satisfactory final result. An absolute apposition of skin edges was demanded, and should he have discovered, after the meticulous insertion of dozens of minute stitches, that this compliance had not been met, or, alternatively, that he had seen a better way of arranging the flaps, the work would be undone and started afresh.

His patience was proverbial and unsurpassed, and he always maintained that the true test of the temperamental suitability of a surgeon to plastic work was his willingness to destroy hours of work to the advantage of the final result of the operation. His dictum was 'Never do today what can honourably be put off until tomorrow'. He would never be persuaded to make a hurried decision or perform a hurried operation, both of which could have irreparably damaged the final appearance of the patient.

Sir Harold was a brilliant and inspiring teacher. He devoted much thought to his teaching technique and had the opportunity to develop his methods to the full. Teaching revolved around the preoperative planning clinics where patients would be seen and the nature of the lesions to be repaired demonstrated. The discussion of the cases, however, did not take place in the restricting presence of the patients, and the courses to be pursued surgically were debated at length in a separate room. He was one of the few teachers who practised what he taught. He stressed always the absolute necessity of handling tissues gently, the extreme importance of accurate edge apposition and the imperative need for careful dressing. In fact, he never failed to apply pressure dressings and bandages himself, for he had learnt through hard experience that badly dressed grafts failed to thrive and sloughed with alarming rapidity.

To describe the face that Sir Harold Gillies presented to the world is not difficult. His idiosyncrasies and appearance made an indelible impression on all who knew him.

He was sometimes irascible, always unpredictable: he was a bon viveur in the truest sense and loved club life at the Garrick and the Junior Carlton. He had an inexhaustible capacity for 'doing things' and was never happier than when painting, fishing, motoring, playing the violin (at which he was most proficient), or working.

His ingenious mind found expression not only in his surgery, but also in the production of innumerable inventions. He patented a revolving car seat, an electric suction razor (in his own words, "a cross between a dermatome and a vacuum cleaner") and a coat hanger. The coat hanger was most successful financially; many were sold in the West End stores during the Christmas shopping period of 1959. Its principal was based on the fact that one always dons ones trousers before the jacket!

He was always known as Giles by his friends, and Giles could always be found in the centre of a laughing group or traced by an endless succession of cigarette stubs. He smoked incessantly even whilst performing minor 'finishing' operations. When patients complained about the impending drop of the accumulated tube of ash, he would say, "Don't you worry, it's perfectly sterile!"

His handwriting was absolutely illegible, and the story of a patient who used one of his prescriptions for everything from a season ticket on the London buses to a free pass to cricket games, boxing matches and horse races is famous. The prescrisption ended its distinguished career by inspiring the patient's daughter in the writing of the opening phrases of an original piano concerto, which won her a two-year scholarship at the London Conservatory of Music.

His suite at the London Clinic where he consulted every

Tuesday displayed evidence of his varying interests and activities. The walls were decorated with a stuffed 12lb Laerdal salmon, the insignia of the Orders of St Olav and Dannebrog, the certificate of Honorary Fellowship of the American College of Surgeons, a signed photograph of Earl Beatty accepting the surrender of the German Grand Fleet in 1918, an etching by Henry Tonks, a photograph of himself on the links whilst playing golf for England and one or two of his current paintings.

The floor staff of the London Clinic always looked forward to his Wednesday operating sessions in Theatre No 3 when his anaesthetist was invariably Sir Ivan Magill.

He was habitually late for appointments and would think nothing of leaving a waiting room full of patients in favour of a game of golf or the promise of some good fishing.

He was devoted to his children into whom he instilled much of the zest for life that he enjoyed. His eldest son, John Gillies MBE, played squash for Cambridge and England. He was a fighter pilot during the Second World War and was shot down during the Battle of Britain, spending until 1945 as a prisoner of war. He is now an accountant practising in South Island of New Zealand. His younger son, Dr Michael Gillies, who followed his father's footsteps at Caius and Barts, is qualified in entomology and tropical medicine and is now working for the Colonial Medical Service. Of his two daughters, one married Professor Harrison, Professor of Anatomy at the London Hospital, and the other is the widow of the late Bill Travers, the oil magnate, and lives mainly in Burma and India.

*

This was Sir Harold Gillies, the man and the surgeon, loved and respected by all who knew him. His colleagues recognised his many talents and forgave his few weaknesses. He was set apart by the broad spectrum of his experience and Mr Patrick Clarkson acknowledges this in writing, "He was a member of a bigger and wider world than that enjoyed by most consultants." He left us secure in the knowledge that he is likely to remain "the greatest world influence of any British surgeon this century".

"Sir Harold Gillies' name might perish but his influence will be immortal."

Biographical Authorities

1. Obituaries in:
   The London Clinic Med. J., 2, April 1961, pp. 46-50
   Lancet, 2, 1960, p. 655
   BMJ, 2, 1960, pp. 866, 948, 1387, 1606
   St Barts. Hosp. J., LXV, March 1961, p. 48
   Sunday Times, September, 1960
   Times, September, 1960

2. Tributes in:
   J. of R.N. Medical Service, XLV, Winter 1959, pp. 2-6
   Brit. J. Plast. Surg., 13, October 1960, pp. 193-194
   Plast. Reconstr. Surg., 27th February 1961, pp. 149-153

3. Press references:

1920
   Daily Express – 4th September

1921
   Daily Mail – 3rd November

1924
   Daily Mirror – 15th January
   Evening Standard – 19th February
   Daily Mail – 3rd April

1925
  Evening Standard – 17th January

1926
  Daily Sketch – 28th May

1932
  Daily Express – 15th December

1933
  Sunday Express – 1st October

1935
  Daily Sketch – 1st December
  Daily Sketch – 28th December

1937
  Daily Mirror – 12th March

1938
  Evening Standard – 7th February
  Daily Herald – 10th February

1940
  Daily Sketch – 16th October
  Evening Standard – 16th December

1941
  Daily Telegraph – 15th January

1945
  Evening News – 7th July
  Evening News – 18th July

1947
  Daily Telegraph – 23rd May

1952
  Daily Telegraph – 15th October

1953
> *Daily Mail* – 15th April

1955
> *Daily Telegraph* – 6th August
> *Evening Standard* – 15th November

1957
> *Star* – 21st March
> *Star* – 1st May
> *Daily Express* – 9th May
> *Daily Telegraph* – 17th June
> *Evening Standard* – 12th September
> *News Chronicle* – 12th November
> *Sunday Times* – 8th December

1958
> *News Chronicle* – 7th October

1959
> *Daily Telegraph* – 12th June
> *Evening Standard* – 29 June
> *Sunday Times* – 12th July
> *Evening Standard* – 31st August
> *Star* – 23rd November

1960
> *Sunday Graphic* – 15th May
> *Star* – 19th July
> *Telegraph* – 19th July
> *Daily Express* – 20th July
> *Daily Express* – 12th September
> *Evening Standard* – 16th November

1961
> *Daily Telegraph* – 1st March

4. Biographical notes in:
   Who's Who
   The Medical Directory

5. Correspondence and personal accounts of life in:
   BMJ, April 25th 1959, p.1100
   BMJ, June 13th 1959, p.1525
   Trans. Med. Soc. Lond., 41, 1917-1918, pp.165-170

6. *Plastic Surgery of the Face*, Gillies and Kelsey Fry, OUP, 1920

7. *Principles and Art of Plastic Surgery*, Gillies, Millard and Magill, Little, Brown and Co, Boston, 1957

8. *McIndoe, Plastic Surgeon*, McLeane, Muller, London, 1961

9. Honours in:
   London Gazette, 1918, 3; 1919, 2; 1930, 1.

10. Also consulted:

B. Adams, Esq.	D. Michael, Esq.
N. K. Harrison, Esq.	H. M. Petty, Esq.
A. Hagenbach, Esq.	Dr I. D. Pringle
J. L. Thornton, Esq.	R. A. W. McDowal, Esq.

11. Case notes of:
    Henry Causer, M 11211, 1922-1923
    Reginald Dickinson, M 10830, 1922-1923

12. The help of the following is gratefully acknowledged:
    The Librarians of The Royal Society of Medicine,
    The Royal College of Surgeons, St Bartholomew's Hospital,
    Wellcome Historical Museum, The Guildhall Library.

The Director, Dept. of Statistics, SBH; The Steward, SBH; The Director, The Registry, SBH; The Staff, Dept. of Medical Photography, SBH

A History of Plastic Surgery

The love of life is next to the love of our own face and thus the mutilated cry for help

– Sushruta Samhita

Sir Harold Gillies' early work was based almost entirely on methods described in medical texts dating back to 600 BC. It is therefore appropriate to briefly consider the sources which were specifically acknowledged by Sir Harold to have been his inspiration.

INDIAN SURGERY

There are written texts in existence recording operations for the repair of noses by flaps taken from the cheek. This technique in rhinoplasty is the oldest known to man and its origin is obscure. Over time there evolved a method based on free skin grafts from the gluteal region. The part of the nose to be covered was patterned from a leaf; a graft of the requisite size was cut from the skin covering the buttocks, and a metallic frame was inserted, with two tubes, into the nostril to support the graft,

And then scraping the border (to which the graft is to be joined) and making the surface fresh (to make the graft successful) the flap is to be carefully sutured. When the graft has been properly made, a powder composed of ptercarpus santalinus, glycyrrhiza glabra and sulphate of antimony, should be sprinkled over the part, and then it should be covered with lint, which is to be kept moistened with oleum sesamum until the complete graft has taken place.

This is the operation as described by Sushruta Samhita, the great Hindu surgeon, working in the 5th century BC. Originally, the method was practised by tile-makers (surgery was a lowly profession in early India), who would have used potters' earth in place of the adhesive powder described by Sushruta. Early practitioners would also use the mouth parts of black ants to approximate the skin edges, whereas Sushruta was versed in the use of horsehair, hemp and flax for the suturing of wounds and incisions.

Sushruta described operations for the repair of lips by means of cheek flaps, and fifteen methods of restoring split or mutilated ear lobes. Of the cheek flap method for restoration of the nose, he writes:

The careful doctor takes (as a pattern) the head of a plant the size of the nose, cuts a flap from the cheek according to the pattern laid upon it, but leaves the flap attached at one place. He quickly puts the (new) nose in place. After he has incised the edges he fastens it in the proper position with a good bandage, carefully inserts two small tubes of appropriate size, elevates it and strews over it dust of red sandalwood, sweet wood and antimony. Then he covers it with white cloth and moistens it often with oil of sesame... When the transplanted flap is united the pedicle is divided. If the nose is too small one attempts to make it grow; if it is too large, one reduces it to the proper size.

Rhinoplasty was an operation much in demand in ancient India as nasal mutilation was punishment for many crimes, including adultery. Sushruta describes yet another method of nasal restoration, utilising the classical forehead flap. The base of the pedicle was situated at the junction of the eyebrows and the flap extended upwards and laterally to one of the temporal regions. The resultant scars of this operation were striking and the pedicles frequently necrosed due to kinking of the stem on its descent from the forehead.

Sushruta was also aware of the finer points of surgery. He writes, "...the incision of a surgeon's knife should never have a distorted or an improper shape... An incision...not made as directed may give rise to extreme pain, prolonged granulations and condylomatous growths."

The first printed account of the Indian methods of rhinoplasty can be found in the anatomical textbook of Alexander Benedictus, 1497.

ROMAN SURGERY

quia nulq̃ celerius cancer occupat, aut difficilius tollit. Ratio cu-
rationis eiufmodi eft. Id quod curatū eft, in quadratum redigere,
ab interioribus eius angulis lineas tranfuerfas incidere, quæ citeri
orem partem ab ulteriore ex toto diducant : deinde ea quæ ficre
pofuimus, in unum adducere. Si non fatis iunguntur, ultra lineas,
quas ante fecimus, alias duas lunatas, & ad plagam conuerfas im-
mittere, quibus fumma tantū cutis diducatur. Sic enim fit, ut faci-
lius quod adducitur, fequi pofsit : quod non ui cogendum eft,
fed ita adducendum, ut ex facili fubfequatur, & dimiffum non
multum recedat. Interdum autem ab altera parte cutis haud om

Extract from Book VII of Chapter IX of Aurelii Corne Lij
Celsi, De Arte Medica Libri *(edited by) Guliemi Pantini
Tiletani, Basileae, 1552*

The work of Aulus Cornelius Celsus (25 BC - 50 AD) was
based on Indian and Alexandrian surgical teaching. In Book
VII of *De Arte Medica*, he describes two methods of covering tissue defects. He writes:

> The method of the cure is this; to reduce that, which is
> mutilated, into a square; from its interior angles to cut in
> transverse lines, so as to divide the part that lies within
> these lines, from that beyond them; then to draw together
> the parts we have thus opened.

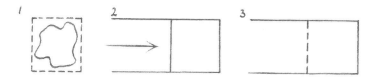

If they (the edges of the wound) do not fully meet, then beyond the lines we have made before, to cut in two places in a lunated form, so as only to separate the surface of the skin; for by this means what we draw together will be more at liberty to follow...

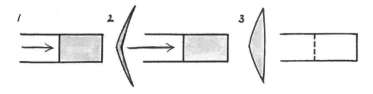

...which is not to be forced together but gently drawn, so as it may easily follow, and when let go, not recede far.

Celsus also described for the first time operations for the relief of ectropion. In old age he states that ectropion can be cured by "burning the excrescence with a slender piece of iron and then anointing with honey."

ITALIAN SURGERY

Gaspare Tagliacozzi (1546-1549), Professor of Surgery and Anatomy at the University of Bologna and Chief Surgeon to the Grand Dukes of Tuscany and Mantua, placed plastic surgery on a secure scientific footing.

Tagliacozzi had been introduced to the speciality through the work of the Brancas, a family of surgeons practising in Sicily during the first half of the fifteenth century. Sicilian rhinoplasty is mentioned in a letter of the poet Elisio Calenzio to a friend:

Orpianus, if you wish to have your nose restored, come here. Really it is the most extraordinary thing in the world. Branca of Sicily, a man of wonderful talent, has found out how to give a person a new nose, which he either builds from the arm or borrows from a slave. When I saw this, I decided to write to you, thinking that no information could be more valuable. Now if you come, I would have you know that you shall return home with as much nose as you please. Fly!

Antonio Branca is mentioned as performing plastic operations by Peter Ranzano, Bishop of Lucerne, in his *Annals of the World* (1442) and by the German Surgeon Heinrich von Pfolspeundt, who was writing in 1460.

The secrets of their technique in reparative surgery were well kept by the Brancas and it is not known how Tagliacozzi learnt of them. However, in 1597, he published *De Curtorum Chirurgia*, the result of many years of practice and experimentation in the transfer of grafts.

This beautifully illustrated book is the first known treatise on plastic surgery and holds a unique position in the history of the art. It describes in detail methods for the reconstruction of the nose, ear auricles and lips.

In 1586 Tagliacozzi wrote to a friend of his rhinoplastic operation, describing the method reiterated seven years later in *De Curtorum Chirurgia*:

...You see, Pareus, Groumelinus and others have written that a hole or cavity is made in the arm, in which the mutilated nose is buried, until flesh grows onto it; that then the flesh is polished off into the shape of a nose. This,

notwithstanding my respect for such eminent men, is far
afield from the techniques of the skill; and we are far from
making use of any flesh (if they interpret muscular tissue as flesh) or from digging out a hole or cavity in the
arm, but rather that an incision, made in the arm, consist
only of a smooth piece of the epidermis, equal in size to
the nose that is to be refashioned, and no use of the flesh
beneath is made in the operation, but only the skin of the
arm is taken in joining it to the nose by the same method
of grafting, which the professors of agriculture have been
wont to call grafting by means of a sprout plucked out of
its own matrix, just as we are stating in our treatise in a
clearer and more illuminating way...

He then proceeds to detail the procedure, which is sum-
marised thus:

After proper preliminary measures had been taken regarding the general health of the patient, he was seated in front
of the surgeon and supported by an assistant. The surgeon closed the broad blades of a specially designed pair
of forceps onto an area of skin overlying the biceps muscle of the left arm (*icon tertia*). A double edged knife was
then passed through horizontal slits in the forceps' blades,
detaching a generously proportioned strip of skin from
the underlying subcutaneous tissue. This area of skin, on
removal of the instruments, was left as a bridge pedicle. A
piece of lint soaked in oil was then placed under the flap
to prevent reunion (*icon quarta*).

The dressing was left for four days after which time
(if infection had not supervened) the pedicle was severed

from the arm at its upper end (*icon quinta*). The flap was then carefully dressed until the under surface had granulated and the skin had contracted to its minimum size.

This usually took a fortnight and the patient was then considered ready to undergo the main operation. He was purged and shaved, and he donned a hooded leather jacket (*icon sexta*). The edges of the flap and the nasal aperture were freshened and one sutured to the other. The arm was kept in a semi-flexed position by the straps (*icon septima*) attached to the leather jacket (*icon octaa* and *icon nona*).

The patient was kept in bed and the ligatures removed on the third to the fifth day. The pedicle was severed from its arm root on the twentieth day (*icon decima*). The new nose was then covered with a special dressing until final trimming (*icon undecima*).

This operation was first performed on Conte Brachetti di Modena in 1580 after luetic destruction of the nose. It was, as may be imagined, an extremely painful process: in 1612 Paulo Zacchias (1584-1659), physician to Popes Innocent X and Alexander VIII, wrote, "If a malefactor was condemned to lose his nose and thereby lost it, it was legal to have it restored by the operation of Tagliacozzi; because the operation could be considered a punishment on account of the time required to perform and the pain occasioned."

Selection of illustrations from *De Curtorum Chirurgia per Institionem*, Gasparis Taliacotti, Bononiensis, Venetiis, 1597

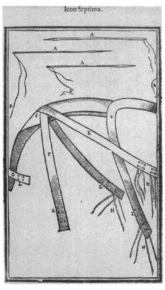

In *De Curtorum Chirurgia*, thirteen chapters are taken up with the discussion of the rationale behind plastic operations. In the fourteenth chapter, donor sites are enumerated, the best for the nose and lips, the arm, and for the ear, the skin behind it. Chapters fifteen and sixteen contain directions regarding the dimensions of the grafts and the ways in which the grafts are united with the recipient areas: Tagliacozzi states that too much skin should be raised, rather than too little. The seventeenth chapter discusses the factors of age, constitution and season in the surgical risk. In the eighteenth chapter he maintains that there is no reason why the skin of one person should not unite with that of another. The nineteenth chapter summarises the ancient techniques in reparative surgery, and in the twentieth, twenty-first and twenty-second, he defends rhinoplasty against the charges of cruelty levelled against it. In the twenty-third chapter, the advantages and disadvantages of different techniques are discussed in the repair of nose, ears and lips, and in the twenty- fourth, the points in which the new nose differs from the original are described. Chapter twenty-five contains a resumé of the whole subject. Tagliacozzi concludes by writing:

> We restore, repair and make whole those parts of the face which nature has given but which fortune has taken away, not so much that they might delight the eye but that they may buoy up the spirit and help the mind of the afflicted.

An extraordinarily enlightened sentiment.

Stress has been laid upon the work of Tagliacozzi, for it is on this that Sir Harold Gillies based many of his rhino-plastic techniques evolved during the First World War.

After his death, Gaspare Tagliacozzi was buried in the Church of St Giovanni Batista, Bologna, but his body was later exhumed after the Roman Catholic Church posthumously excommunicated him. The Church, in fact, had adopted strong views against the practice of plastic surgery, maintaining that mutilation, whether by disease or by trauma, was the will of God. Plastic surgery fell into disrepute and was not revived in Europe until the closing years of the eighteenth century.

EUROPEAN SURGERY

In the October edition of the *Gentleman's Magazine*, 1794, there appeared the following description of the Hindu operation of rhinoplasty:

> Cowasjee, a Mahratta, of the caste of husbandmen, was a bullock-driver with the English army in the war of 1792 and was made a prisoner by Tippoo, who cut off his nose and one of his hands. In this state he joined the Bombay army near Seringapatam and is now a pensioner of the Honourable East India Company. For about twelve months he was wholly without a nose; when he had a new one put on by a Mahratta surgeon, a Kumar, near Poonah ... Two of the medical gentlemen, Mr Thomas Cruso and Mr James Findlay, of Bombay, had seen it performed as follows: A thick plate of wax is fitted to the stump of the nose so as

to make a nose of good appearance; it is then flattened and laid on the forehead. A line is drawn around the wax which is then of no further use; and the operator then dissects off as much skin as it covered, leaving undivided a small slip between the eyes. This slip preserves the circulation, till a union has taken place between the new and the old parts. The cicatrix of the stump of the nose is next pared off; and immediately behind this raw part, an incision is made through the skin, which passes round both alae, and goes along the upper lip. The skin is now brought down from the forehead; and being twisted half round, its edge is inserted into this incision; so that a nose is formed with a double fold, above and with its alae and septum below, fixed in the incision. A little Terra Japonica is softened with water and being spread on slips of cloth, five or six of these are placed over each other, to secure the joining. No other dressing than this cement is used for four days; it is then removed, and cloths are dipped in ghee (a kind of butter) are applied. The connecting slip of skin is divided about the twenty-fifth day; when a little more dissecting is necessary to improve the appearance of the nose. For five or six days after the operation, the patient is made to lie on his back; and on the tenth day, bits of soft cloth are put into the nostrils to keep them sufficiently open. This operation is always successful. The artificial nose is secure and looks nearly as well as the natural one; nor is the scar on the forehead very observable, after a length of time.

This awakened wide interest in plastic surgery and in 1814, Joseph Constantine Carpue (1764-1846), an English surgeon, reported the successful completion of two rhinoplastic operations which improved on the Hindu methods by adding a septum nasi.

Carpue wrote a paper in 1816 discussing the various known methods of transferring tissue, where he points out the misconception in Tagliacozzi's claim that the skin of one person will unite with that of another.

John Hunter had worked on the transplantation of tissue in animals and Dieffenbach (1792-1847) continued the experiments. The foundations of the rationale behind the grafting of bone were thus elucidated.

1809:   Carl von Graefe (1787-1840) described a successful case of blepharoplasty. He repaired the lower eyelid by means of a pedicle flap from the cheek based on the Hindu method.

1814:   William Balfour published his paper, 'Observations on adhesion with two Cases, Demonstrative of the Powers of Nature to Reunite Parts which have been, by Accident, Totally Separated from the Animal System.' He wrote,

> I am convinced that had Taliacotus at once separated from the system, the flaps of skin with which he repaired mutilated parts, his operation would have been equally successful, infinitely less troublesome to himself and distressing to his patients... Attempts at reunion of divided parts may be successful.

1816:   Von Graefe introduced the first surgical techniques for the repair of the soft palate (staphylorrhoplasty).

1821: F. L. G. Fricke (1790-1842) published *Die Bildung neuer Augenlider - Blepharoplastik*, an extensive treatise on the use of pedicle grafts from the parietal and cheek region to supply skin for the reconstruction of deformed eye-lids.

1824: A case of rhinoplasty, as performed by a Mr Travers, was reported in the *Lancet*. The account concludes, "This operation is called the Taliacotian, from the name of its original inventor."

1827: 'A Case in which a Lost Nose Was Restored' appears in the *Edinburgh Medical and Surgical Journal* (Vol. XXVIII). This article concludes,

> This curious operation is occasionally practised in India by the native practitioners. Dr M. Whirter, who paid great attention to their surgery during a long journey in the East ... informs us that these operators are in the habit of pummelling the integuments of the forehead with the heel of their slippers, so as to excite the circulation before performing their incisions.

1840: Robert Liston (1794-1847) described Indian methods of rhinoplasty in his *Elements of Surgery*.

c.1840: Conrad Martin Langenbeck (1776-1851) described methods for repairing cleft palates.

c.1850: Auguste Nélaton (1807-1873) described a total rhinoplasty utilising costal cartilage for the formation of the new septum.

1858: Louis Ollier (1825-1900) reported on experimental work concerning bone grafts.

1859: Joseph-François Malgaigne (1806–1865) described

cleavage lines of the skin in his textbook on surgical anatomy and experimental surgery. Langer investigated this phenomenon fully.

1869: J. C. F. Guyon (1831-1920) first reported the success of pinch grafts to a granulating defect.

1869: Jacques-Louis Reverdin (1842-1929) demonstrated that a completely detached piece of human epidermis could continue to live and grow when placed on a properly prepared recipient area. (*Bulletin de la Societe de Chirurgia*, Dec. 15th 1869).

1872: Ollier announced novel method of skin grafting. The *Bulletin de L'Academia de Medicine* stated:

> Instead of grafting small pieces of 2-3cm² and 4mm², as is done by M. Reverdin, M. Ollier takes large pieces from 4-8 cm² and more, including not only the superficial layers of the skin but the whole dermis.

1874: Carl Thiersch (1822-1895) first suggested the use of a razor in cutting grafts and emphasized the necessity of shaving the fat underneath the graft. (*Verh. Deutsch. Gessel. F Chirurgie*, 1874). Hence the Ollier-Thiersch graft.

1875: J. R. Wolfe (1824–1904) of Glasgow described methods for grafting of conjunctivae in 1872, and later, methods for repairing eye-lid defects, including ectropion, with full-thickness grafts devoid of fat. Fedor Krause subsequently modified the technique. Hence the Wolfe-Krause graft.

1891: D. F. Keegan of Bengal described his rhinoplastic operation in the *Lancet*:

> I generally allow at least a fortnight or three weeks to elapse after the mutilation before attempting to restore a new nose. A day or two before the operation I prepare a pattern of the forehead flap by cutting it out first in a piece of a leaf of the plantain (banana tree). A piece of stout brown paper, cut to the exact size of this pattern is rendered adhesive on one side by smearing it with litharge plaster, and at the proper stage of the operation is stuck firmly on the forehead in a slanting direction.

He recognised the importance of lining the new nose to prevent the withering that otherwise takes place.

1898: Vercher described his mammaplastic technique. He reduced the breast substance by the excision of a quadrant in toto.

1903: Morestin described his mammaplastic technique. A curvilinear incision was made in the sub-mammary fold and the breast tissue exposed. Adequate quantities of tissue were removed and the reshaped breast anchored with deep cat-gut sutures to the pectoral fascia.

HISTORICAL AUTHORITIES

1. *Aurelii Corne Lij, de Arte Medica Libri,* edited by Gulielmi Pantini Tiletani, Basileae, 1552
2. *Aulus Cornelius Celsus, Of Medicine,* translated and edited by James Greive, MD, 1838
3. *De Curtorum Chirurgia Per Institionem,* by Gaspare Tagliacozzi, published by Gaspar Biononus, Venice, 1597
4. *Gentleman's Magazine,* October, 1794
5. *Evolution of Plastic Surgery,* Maxwell Maltz, Froben Press, New York, 1946
6. *The Early History of Surgery,* W J Bishop, Robert Hale Ltd, 1960
7. *Plastic Surgery of the Face,* Gillies and Kelsey Fry, OUP, 1920
8. *Principles and Art of Plastic Surgery,* Gillies, Millard and Magill, Little, Brown and Co, Boston, 1957
9. The help of the following is gratefully acknowledged: The Librarians, St Bartholomew's Hospital, Wellcome Historical Museum

A Synopsis of the
Published Works of
Sir Harold Gillies

1916 – 1917

1. Some cases of facial deformity treated in the Department of Plastic Surgery at the Cambridge Hospital, Aldershot.

St Barts. Hosp. J., 24, 1916-1917, pp. 79-83

Case 1
Formation of upper half of the bridge of nose.

Loss of tissue:

1.   Entire nasal bony structure
2.   Skin covering upper part of nose
3.   Right eye

1st Operation (June 14th, 1916): Excision of scar, bridge formed by portion of perpendicular plate of ethmoid and two sliding advancement flaps sutured over defect.
Result: On contraction of skin flaps, the bridge collapsed.

2nd Operation (September 3rd, 1916): Small skin incision made into which was inserted a piece of costal cartilage of suitable dimensions.

Result: On fitting of artificial right eye, appearance was highly satisfactory.

Case 2
Temporal muscle transplantation for deformities caused by loss of malar bone.

Remarks: Depressed scars can be remedied by fat and cartilage grafts or foreign bodies, such as celluloid or wax.

Fat grafts are uncertain; they are liable to become infected. Celluloid plates are unsatisfactory.

Uniformly good results are achieved with temporal muscle flaps. Incision is in hairy scalp and is disguised. The transplanted muscle is sutured to the deep tissues under eye and can easily be made to contract.

Case 3
Formation of new corners of the mouth, together with the repair of the adjacent portions of lips and cheek; fracture of the jaw.

1st Operation (September 11th, 1916): Excision of scars. Defects repaired by direct apposition of edges and cheek flaps.
Result: Cosmetic appearance good. Parts of wound broke down due to movement of lower jaw. Since this, care has been taken to immobilise lower jaw until wounds have fully healed.

2nd Operation (October 31st, 1916): Scar re-excised in order to raise corner of mouth.

3rd Operation (January 1st, 1917): Final adjustments performed. Scar re-excised and fat flaps transferred to fill depression under scar.

1917 – 1918

1. Formation of the upper half of the bridge of the nose.

J. Laryng., 32, 1917, pp. 274-283

Principles restated as above (Case 1)

2. Two cases illustrating plastic and dental treatment.

Lancet, 1917, 1, pp. 850-852

Discussion of cases to appear later in *Plastic Surgery of the Face.*

3. Mechanical supports in plastic surgery (with L. A. R. King).

Lancet, 1917, 1, pp. 412-414

Mechanical supports discussed in *Plastic Surgery of the Face.*

4. Problems of facial reconstruction.

Trans. Med. Soc. Lond., 41, 1917-1918, pp. 165-170

1. A biographical account of war career.
2. Discussion of plastic cases from Sidcup accompanied by slides demonstrating results.
3. Discussion of dental treatment associated with plastic surgery.

5. Demonstration in rhinoplasty

Trans. Roy. Soc. Med., 11, i-ii, 1918, *Sect. Laryng.*, pp. 87-90

Loss of Nose:

Class 1: Loss of portion of the lip or the alar.
Methods of repair: By free skin graft, Keegan-Smith Indian method or cheek flap.

Class 2: Loss of upper quarter of the nasal bridge.
Method of repair: Lining mucous membrane is of no importance. An osteoperiostral flap was turned down from the frontal region to support the forehead flap.

Class 3: Loss of upper half of the major bridge.
Methods of repair:
1. Cheek flaps with later embedding of a cartilage graft.
2. Cheek flaps with support of graft from tibia. This was not satisfactory.
3. Cartilage support was embedded in forehead in forehead flap before this was swung down. (Capt. Hett).

Class 4: Loss of lower third of nose.
Method of repair: Modification of Keegan-Smith operation.

Class 5: Pug nose.
Methods of repair: Cartilage is embedded in upper part of nose which was later moved down to support tip. The defect thus formed was repaired with a forehead flap.

6. Discussion on plastic operations of the eyelids.

Trans. Ophthal. Soc. UK, 48, 1918, pp. 70-99

This is treated fully in *Plastic Surgery of the Face*.

1920

1. Plastic Surgery of facial burns.

Surg. Gynec. Abstet., 30, 1920, pp. 121-134

A paper read before the Clinical Congress of the American College of Surgeons, New York City, October 20-24th 1919.

General character of burns:

1. Acid burn: Collection of deep burns of small areas, joined by less severely affected, and even normal, patches of skin.
2. Airman's burn: Similar to cordite burn and resembles acid burn. Differences are due to types of clothing worn (helmets, goggles, caps, scarves, etc.).
3. Flame burn: All show deformity of eyelids with a greater or lesser degree of ectropion. Many degrees of burn, the most severe destroying all skin and exposing muscle layers.

Treatment:

Early: No opinion on best early treatment.
Intermediate: Measures to reduce fibrosis, ie diathermy, ion-

ization, massage, and protection by a greasy mask. More potent measures; filtered x-ray and radium, but this jeopardises the success of surgery.

Final or Plastic: Commenced after scar has ceased to contract (best time interval is one year).

A general plan of reconstruction must be formulated, after accurate determination of tissue loss.

Complete facial replacement procedure:

1. Forehead is replaced by a Wolfe graft.
2. Eyebrows are grafted from area of hairy scalp above mastoid region.
3. Movable eyelids are provided by author's 'epithelial outlay' operation - an adaptation of the Esser inlay.
4. Nose is renovated by a Wolfe graft, after excision of scar tissue, or by a tubed pedicle from chest or neck.
5. Upper lip is revived by a whole depth hair-bearing graft from scalp.
6. Cheek, chin and lower lip are replaced by a tubed pedicle from neck and chest.
7. Ears are replaced by two layers of skin enclosing shaped cartilage.
8. Hands repaired by direct abdominal flap, by Thiersch grafting or by tubed pedicle.

Methods of grafting (tubed pedicle, Wolfe-Thiersch graft) are then discussed.

The Tubed Pedicle:

Propounded by the author in September 1917 when he was first confronted with the most serious type of facial burn.

Stage 1: The base of the pedicle lies at the upper part of the neck; it measures 2 to 3 inches in width. Two parallel cuts are made down the neck and over the clavicle to the area which is to be transferred to the face. If this area is large, it is advisable to have two pedicles, one on either side of the neck, the flap proper being situated centrally.

The area of neck skin outlined by the parallel incisions is raised by undercutting. The two skin edges are now brought together and sutured forming the tubed pedicle. The defect under the pedicle is repaired by approximating the edges of the wound and tension suturing (the edges are undercut to facilitate this). If this cannot be achieved, Thiersch grafting is indicated.

Stage 2: (Any time after 3 weeks). The flap proper is outlined, raised from the chest and grafted onto the required area of the face. The secondary raw area is Thiersch grafted.

The submanibular area supplies the best blood supply to the pedicle through its base (the location of the anastomosis between transversalis colli and suprascapular vessels).

This stage is dangerous. It should be recognised that the blood supply of the pedicle, before the flap is raised, may be upwards from the chest to prevent sloughing; the flap proper should be partly raised and tubed prior to final detachment.

Stage 3: The final operation consists of disposing of the pedicle.

Two alternatives:

1. The pedicle is cut close to the face, opened out and returned to the space it occupied previously.
2. The pedicle is cut close to the neck attachment and applied to the face.

The pedicle is hardy with a submandibular blood supply and can be moved three or four times. It resists the effects of kinking well.

The method has fascinating possibilities in the repair of the penis and the breast.

2. Plastic Surgery of the Face

Gillies and Kelsey Fry, *OUP*, 1920

Chapter I: Principles

1. *History*. An accurate history of the injury is shown to be essential, and the importance of determining the healing powers of the patient is stressed.
2. *Examination*. The exact extent of the loss of tissue is determined; this may be more than is immediately apparent.

   Loss is classified:
   i. Mucous lining
   ii. Bony or cartilaginous support

iii. Skin covering

A plaster cast is made of the face and the features reconstructed on this. With radiographs to differentiate between loss and displacement, the surgeon now has adequate data upon which to make a diagnosis.

3. *Treatment.* All normal tissue should be replaced as early as possible and retained in its usual position. In the planning of the operation, function is the first consideration; this, in fact, gives the best cosmetic results.

The restoration is designed from within outwards: the lining membrane must be considered first, then the supporting structure, and finally the skin covering. It is noted that a 'plastic' nose rapidly withers without a lining membrane (Keegan, 1891).

Lining Membrane should be of mucous membrane where possible, otherwise of skin transferred by flaps or pedicles.

Esser Epithelical Inlay is a method of lining sulci with skin (especially labiolingual sulcus). The method was first described by Esser in *Annals of Surgery*, 1917, and was adapted and simplified by the author: a stent mould is wrapped in a thin Thiersch graft and applied to defect *per oram*. It is kept in position by a dental splint.

Supporting Structures. Foreign Body support is condemned. The use of bone grafts has been narrowed down to replacement of malar and mandibular loss. Cartilage is obtained by a variation of the Nélaton method: the graft is directly applied to the site or is buried in the lining graft (not, as Nélaton suggested, in the skin flap).

Fat and muscle grafts are used for obtaining softer contours.

Covering Tissues are supplied by thin Thiersch or whole-thickness Wolfe grafts.

Alternatively skin is transferred by advancement ('Simple', 'V-Y' and 'swinging': *cf.* Celsus), transposition ('embedded') and bridge flaps (simple and tubed pedicle).

The viability of flaps is discussed.

4. *Anaesthesia* (Captain R Wade)

    Plastic operations are long and patients are usually bad anaesthesia risks due to nature of wounds and ill- nourishment.

    Methods:

    i.   Intra-tracheal anaesthesia for extensive operations is the method of choice. Ether is propelled through a catheter by a stream of oxygen or air under positive pressure
    ii. Nasal tube anaesthesia is used in smaller operations
    iii. Chloroform and oxygen is applied in a sitting-up position in cases of lip and mandible surgery

5. *Operation*

It is bad practice to use tissue forceps on skin edges.

The skin is prepared with ether and iodine or methylated spirit.

Warning is given of the dangers of inhalation of blood and mucus. The amount of shock suffered by the patient depends upon the area of skin disturbed.

Simple Advancement Flap:

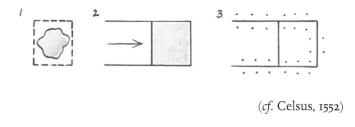

(*cf.* Celsus, 1552)

"Y-Y" Advancement Flap:

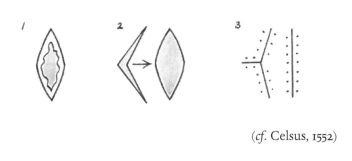

(*cf.* Celsus, 1552)

"Swinging" Advancement Flap:

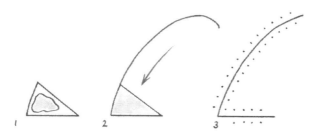

Original wound must have healed soundly before reparative surgery is undertaken: the condition of the upper respiratory tract must be above suspicion and the skin must be free of pimples and acne pustules.

An operation usually takes two or more stages. The importance of pressure dressing to the graft is stressed.

The simplest operation in plastic work is the excision of a scar.

Suture. The importance of a smooth technique and dexterity is stressed. The author's instrument is described and illustrated.

The material used in cuticular suturing is horse hair, which is valuable owing to its elasticity: it is also used in subcuticular suturing, as catgut produces a 'heaped-up edge'.

Invisible scars. The factors concerned in the production of the optimum scar are:

i. Asepsis
ii. Avoidance of tension
iii. Perfect apposition of skin edges
iv. An often unknown personal factor in the patient
v. Early removal of sutures

Dressings. Hot saline packs are valuable in the case of a flap or graft of doubtful viability.

6. *After Treatment.* The apposing sutures are removed on the fourth or fifth day. The retaining sutures are left until their function is fulfilled.

Massage is useful in dispersing oedema in newly made flaps and is indicated as a routine measure in assisting the restoration of function.

A close watch is kept on the site of the operation for the first forty-eight hours: prompt action may save an unhealthy graft.

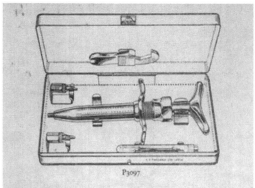

P3097

GILLIES' ANÆSTHETIC SYRINGE, for local anæsthesia, consisting of 60 min. all metal syringe, two adapters, tube of six Schimmel's needles and spanner, in chromium plated case .. .. each
Spare Schimmel's Needles, ·45 mm. by 45 mm., in tubes of six needles, per tube

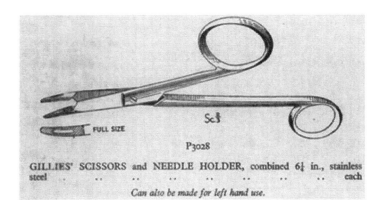

P3028

GILLIES' SCISSORS and NEEDLE HOLDER, combined 6¼ in., stainless
steel .. .. each

Can also be made for left hand use.

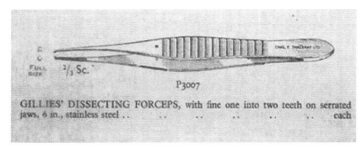

P3007

GILLIES' DISSECTING FORCEPS, with fine one into two teeth on serrated
jaws, 6 in., stainless steel .. .. each

Electrical treatment (vibro-massage, diathermy, ionisation, x-rays) is routine.

Early active movements are encouraged.

"In conclusion, it may be said that Time is the plastic surgeon's greatest ally, and at the same time his most trenchant critic."

Chapter II: Repair of the Cheek

1. Depressed Scars are defined as those associated with such small loss of tissue that the majority of them may be repaired by excision of the scar, under-cutting the skin and approximation, without the necessity of cutting flaps.

    These are usually caused by missile entry or exit wounds.

2. Wounds of the Cheek with Loss of Soft Tissue only are depressed scars of a more severe nature. They require flap repair.

3. Wounds of the Cheek with Loss of Soft Tissue and Bone.
    i.   Destruction of the malar prominence is treated by a subcutaneous temporal muscle flap covered by a celluloid plate.
    ii. Destruction of the superior maxillary bones is made good by cartilage implants.
    iii. Destruction of the mandible. (*Vide*: Injuries to lower lip).

Case 142

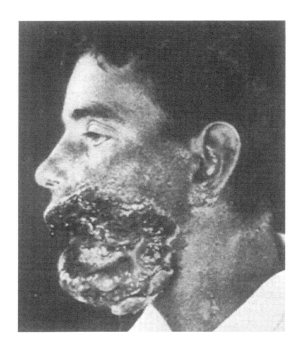

*Early condition of Private RC of the Scottish Rifles
wounded on 1.9.16*

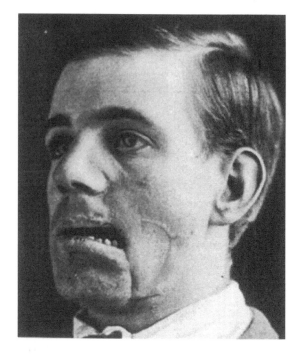

Result of two plastic operations on 10.10.16 and 3.1.17

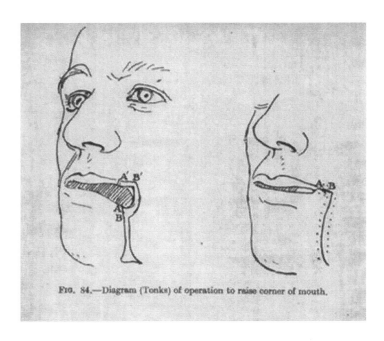

Fig. 84.—Diagram (Tonks) of operation to raise corner of mouth.

135

Chapter III: Injuries of the Upper Lip

These are treated by:

1. Ascending Flaps
    i.   Advantages: Hair-bearing; ample underlying mucous membrane; wide mouth.
    ii. Disadvantages: Blood supply not good due to twisting of flap; muscular movement indifferent; scars noticeable.

2. Descending Flaps
    i.   Advantages: Good blood supply, muscular movement good; scar negligible.
    ii. Disadvantages: No hair; mucous membrane lining apt to be cut too short.

3. Combination of Ascending and Descending Flaps for extensive tissue loss.

4. Temporal Artery Scalp Flap
    i.   Advantages: Provides moustache; no secondary scars on face; lining provided at the same time by inclusion of non-hairy scalp.
    ii. Disadvantages: Blood supply not reliable; no musculature in flap; operation extensive.

The vermillion border of the lip is produced by the grafting of mucous membrane which retains its colour but loses its mucous secreting powers when exposed to air for any length of time.

Case 525

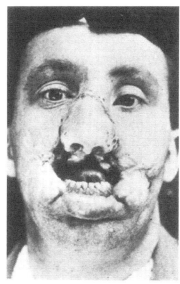

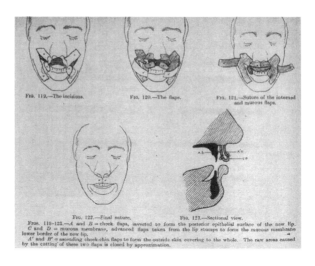

Fig. 119.—The incisions.

Fig. 120.—The flaps.

Fig. 121.—Suture of the internal and mucous flaps.

Fig. 122.—Final suture.

Fig. 123.—Sectional view.

Figs. 119-123.—*A* and *B* = cheek flaps, inverted to form the posterior epithelial surface of the new lip. *C* and *D* = mucous membrane, advanced flaps taken from the lip stumps to form the mucous membrane lower border of the new lip.

A' and *B'* = ascending cheek-chin flaps to form the outside skin covering to the whole. The raw areas caused by the cutting of these two flaps is closed by approximation.

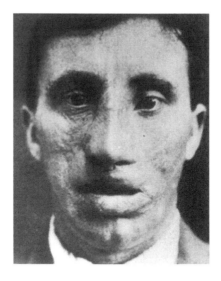

Result of operations utilizing descending and ascending flaps, and inturned flaps. A prosthetic appliance replaced the maxillary defect.

Chapter IV: Injuries of the Lower Lip and Chin

In planning repair of lip, first consideration is for the provision of an adequate bed for a denture.

Cases in which the mandible has been damaged are invariably so severe that no plastic operation has as yet been devised to give anything approaching a satisfactory result: the condition is analogous to the loss of a limb.

The commonest injury to the lower lip is of the 'harelip' variety. This is easily repaired by advancement flaps from surrounding tissue.

Bone Grafting of the Mandible

A piece of the 7th or 8th rib is taken including the costochondral junction and the point of maximum convexity. The bony portion is wired to the freshened anterior fragment of the mandible; the maximum point of convexity forms the new angle and the ascending ramus is represented by the costal cartilage.

Case 188

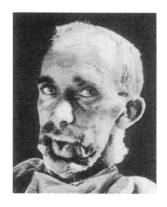

Early condition showing loss of more than half of the lower lip and displacement of the remnants. There was a 2 inch defect of the mandible.

*Healed condition of the wounds.
(This is an example of the work of Professor Tonks:
a pastel sketch.)*

After plastic operation and bone graft.
The scar was excised and advancement flaps covered the defect.

Chapter V: Prosthetic Appliances in Relation
to Plastic Surgery

The use of prostheses was developed by Captain Kelsey Fry, MC, RAMC.

A mould of the defect and its relationships to surrounding hard and soft tissues was made, and the permanent appliance modelled on this.

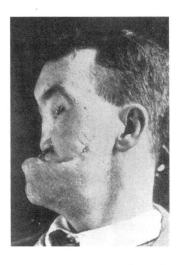

Case showing extensive bony loss of maxilla.

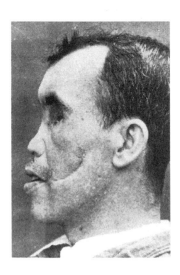

*Result of repair and application of adjustable prosthesis
introduced between upper lip and remains of hard palate.*

Chapter VI: Injuries of the Nose

Group I
Minor injuries to upper quarter of the bridge of the nose. Treated by advancement flaps and turn down osteo-periostial flaps.

Group II
Destruction of upper half of nasal bridge, producing 'bird beak' deformity. Treated by local flaps containing cartilage grafts.

Group III
Destruction of the bridge without distortion of the tip or serious loss of mucous membrane. A cartilage graft is implanted.

Group IV
Loss of middle portions of the bridge. The cartilage graft is embedded in the flap to replace the mucous membrane defect.

Group V
Loss of the alar and lower third of the nose. According to severity, a Wolfe graft or a total rhinoplasty is performed. The rhinoplastic operations used are of Italian or Indian kind.

Case 132

*Healed state of the wound showing total
loss of nasal structure.*

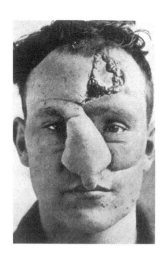

*A forehead flap with cartilage implant swung down to
form the new nose.*

Final appearance showing results of corrective operations.

Chapter VII: Injuries in the Region of the Eyes

Class 1: Injuries of the Orbital Ring are treated by osteo-periostial grafts and shaped cartilage implants. The services of a sculptor are sought to help in the design of the implants.

Class 2: Injuries to the Eyelids are treated by blepharoplasty: free grafts, ascending and descending flaps and tubed pedicles are utilised.

Class 3: Injuries to the Socket are treated by osteo-periostial grafts and the eye replaced with a synthetic globe. Wherever possible the internal muscles of the eye are preserved, a cartilage graft attached to them and a glass 'front' placed on this so that the 'eye' moves.

Treatment of Burns. This subject has been discussed above.

Case 364

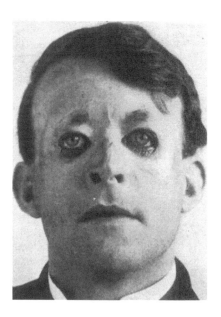

Healed condition showing marked ectropion and scarring of forehead.

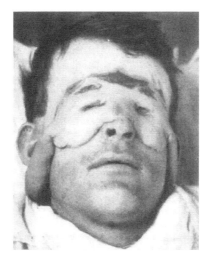

Flap raised from chest on two tubed pedicles.

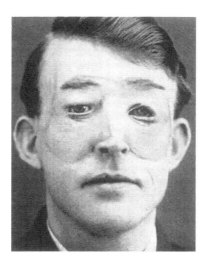

Final appearance. Ectropion relieved. Eyebrows free skin graft from scalp.

Chapter VIII: Plastic Surgery in Civil Cases

The techniques developed during the War are discussed in relation to their use in civilian practice.

---

3. Present day plastic operations of the face.

J. Nat. Dent. Ass. Huntingdon, Ind., 7, 1920, pp. 3-36

Discussion of techniques developed during the war as applied to civilian practice.

4. The tubed pedicle in plastic surgery.

NY Med. J., III, 1920, pp. 1-4

Discussion of the applications of the tubed pedicle technique.

1921 — 1922

1. A new principle in the surgical treatment of 'congenital cleft palate' and its mechanical counterpart.

Gillies and Kelsey Fry, *BMJ*, 1921, 1, pp. 335-338

Ideals to be aimed at are:

1. Perfect speech
2. Perfect mastication
3. Normal nasal respiratory function
4. A normal bony contour

A discussion of the advantages and disadvantages of other techniques in cleft palate repair follows.

Treatment recommended by authors:

It is considered that closure by means of an efficient dental plate is by far the most simple and efficient mode of treatment. There is no interference with the growth of the maxilla or the eruption of teeth.

The soft palate is repaired by approximation and suture of the two halves as far back in the pharynx as possible.

The repair should ideally be completed before the development of speech.

2.

1. Case of depressed bony ridge of nose.

2. Case of depressed fracture of nasal arch.

3. Depressed fracture of nasal and associated bones.

Proc. Roy. Soc. Med., 16, i-ii, 1922-1923, pp. 4-8

These cases were described by H.D. Gillies during a discussion on the methods of repair of the deformity of the nose due to trauma.

Cartilage grafts are preferred by the author for support of the nasal tissues.

———————

1923

1. Deformities of the syphilitic nose.

BMJ, 1923, II, pp. 977-979

Class I: Loss of cartilaginous support. Treated by cartilage implant.

Class II: Typical syphilitic nose: loss of mucous membrane and osteo-cartilaginous support. The mucous membrane is replaced by a thin Thiersch graft.

The skin is divided from underlying bone and the nose is pulled out, revealing a raw area internally which is devoid of mucous membrane lining.

A cap splint is made to fit the front teeth by a dental surgeon. Wires with expanded ends are fitted to the appliance.

Pliable dental modelling composition is inserted into nasal cavity *per oram*, ie through incision made in the sulcus between maxilla and upper lip.

This mould is withdrawn and the Thiersch graft stretched onto it. It is then reinserted and kept in place by the dental appliance.

The appliance is removed when the graft has taken, and, two months later, the bridge is reconstructed with a cartilage implant.

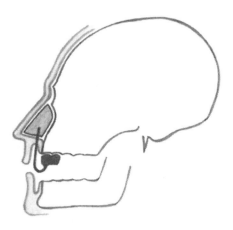

Class III: Loss incurred in typical syphilitic nose but with the complicating feature of skin loss.

The nose is incised horizontally in its mid portion so that the tip can be pulled forward into its normal position. The defect thus produced is filled by

1. Local flaps to construct lining.
2. Tubed pedicle or forehead flap to construct the covering.

A cartilage implant is later made to form the bridge.

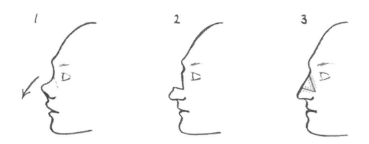

2. The 'eternal (plastic) triangle'. A simple cure.

Lancet, 1923, II, pp. 930-931

The closure of a triangular skin defect is discussed.

The author's method of closing this defect is propounded which is illustrated thus:

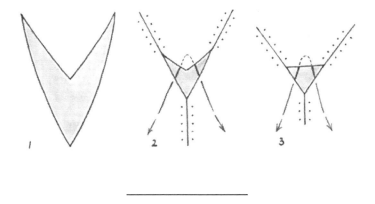

1924 – 1927

1. Plastic Surgery in H. W. Carson's *Modern Operative Surgery*.

Vol. 2, 1929, pp. 368-402

(4th edition edited by G Grey Turner and LC Rogers, Vol. 2, 1959, pp. 1945-2021)

1st Edition 1924:

1. Diagnosis
2. Record taking - Plaster casts, photographs, x-rays
3. General principles
4. Incisions
5. Tissue trauma
6. Haemostasis
7. Deep sutures - catgut by near-far-near method
8. Skin sutures - fine silkworm-gut, by continuous lock or blanket methods
9. Skin grafting - Thiersch, Wolfe
10. Fat-grafting
11. Cartilage grafts
12. Bone-grafting
13. The Gillies tubed pedicle flap

14. Other forms of flaps - advancement and transposed
15. Rhinoplasty
16. Restoration of the bridge of the nose
17. Reduction of prominence of the nasal bridge
18. Plastic operations on eyelids and eyebrows
19. Temporal muscle swings
20. Cicatricial ectropion
21. Plastic operations on ears
22. Plastic operations on lips
23. Harelip
24. Cleft palate

4th Edition, 1956:
(by Sir Harold Gillies and John Barron)

The following sections remain unaltered from 1st edition:

1. Introductory
2. Diagnosis
3. Record Taking
4. General Principles

Additional sections on:

1. Planning of operation - use of templates
2. *Table I.* Time Factor in Acromio-pectoral Flap to Cheek
   Table II. Time Factor in Abdominal Flap to Cheek
   Table III. Free grafts
3. Pressure methods of grafting – Coelst method of stretching graft over celluloid plate

4. Lymphoedema – *to be mentioned later*
5. Deformation of upper limb – burns, loss of digits, syndactilism, Dupytren's contraction
6. Syphilitic nose – *to be mentioned later*
7. Fractures of the face
8. Cosmetic reduction operations, nose and breasts
9. Chronic radio-dermatitis and radio-neurosis – *to be mentioned later*

2. Fractures of the malar-zygomatic compound: with a description of a new x-ray position

by HD Gillies, T Pomfret Kilner, and Sudley Stone.

Brit J. Surg., 14, 1926-1927, pp. 651-656

1. *Discussion of definition, diagnosis and other methods of treatment*

2. *Author's technique*
A small incision is made in the temporal region through the temporal fascia. An elevator is passed down underneath the depressed bone and is used as a lever to manipulate displaced bone into its normal position.

Fixation is achieved by a pad strapped to the face below the malar prominence.

1929 – 1932

1. Cleft palate: hare-lip.

in Garrod and Batten's
Diseases of Children, 1929, pp. 162-169

Discussion of congenital face defects and their treatment.

2. Symblepharon: its treatment by Thiersch and mucous membrane grafting.

Gillies and Pomfret Kilner
Trans.Ophthal. Soc. UK, 49, 1929, pp.470-478

Treatment of the condition in which there is adhesion of one or both eyelids to the eyeball by Esser inlays of mucous membrane or Thiersch grafted skin.

3. The treatment of the broken nose

Gillies and Pomfret Kilner, *Lancet*, 1929, 1, pp. 147-149

Diagnosis, varieties of fracture and complications of the broken nose are discussed.

Aim of the operation is to:

i.   Displace both frontal processes
ii. Disimpact both nasal bones and bring them forward
iii. Straighten the septum
iv. Push in frontal processes and mould whole arch with fingers

———————————

1932 – 1933

1. The design of direct pedicle flaps

BMJ, 1932, II, p. 1008

2. Hare-lip: operations for the correction of secondary deformities.

Gillies and Pomfret Kilner, *Lancet*, 1932, II, pp. 1369-1375

i.   Readjustment of general contour by application of buccal inlay using dental appliance.
ii. Deficient lip margin treated by cupid's bow graft of mucous membrane.
iii. Depressed tip of nose and broad, flat lobule treated by incision of tip of septum and advancement.

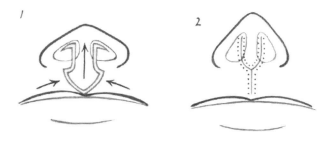

3. The late surgical complications of fracture of the mandible.

Gillies and AH McIndoe,
BMJ, 1933, II, pp. 1060-1063

i.   *Mal-union* treated by osteotomy and bone grafting.
ii. *Delayed union* treated by removal of all foci of infection, drainage of abscesses and interdental fixation.
iii. *Non-union* treated by removal of fibrotic tissue between bone ends and resplinting.
     Loss of bone substance treated by bone-grafting by pedicle graft, block tibial graft, osteo-periostial graft, osteo-chondral rib graft (Gillies, 1919) and ilial graft.

4. Plastic surgery in chronic radiodermatitis and radionecrosis.

Gillies and McIndoe,
Brit. J. Radiol., 6, 1933, pp. 132-147

Groups of Cases:

i. Patients who have received a single dose of x-rays or radium for diagnosis or treatment.
ii. Patients who have undergone treatment for a chronic condition, and who have received small but oft-repeated doses for a long period, often resulting in ulceration.

iii. Professional workers with x-ray apparatus suffering from burns of the hands and face.

Indications for operation:

i. Pain, itching, ulceration and discharge
ii. Deformity from contraction
iii. Cosmetic appearance
iv. Epithelimatous change

Treatment:

i. Excision of area
ii. Application of
    Thick razor-grafts, full-thickness dissected grafts and direct flaps and tubed pedicles

———————————

1933 – 1935

1. Experiences with fascia lata grafts in the operative treatment of facial paralysis.

Proc. Roy. Soc. Med., 27, ii, 1933-4, *Sect. Laryng.*, also *J. Laryng.*, 49, 1934, pp. 743-756

1. *Objects of operation*:
   It is a palliative operation. Fascia lata graft will act as a splint to counteract the overaction of opposing muscles.

2. *Resumé of previous work*

3. *Method of taking graft*:

   i. *Open method*. The graft is taken through a long incision on lateral aspect of the thigh.
   ii. *Closed method*. The graft is taken through a small incision by using the ring-stripper and fascia cutter.

4. *Methods of application*:
   The loops of fascia lata are passed around the paralysed facial muscles at one or more of following points:
   i.   Centre of lower lip
   ii. Corner of mouth
   iii. Centre of upper lip

iv. Round the palpebral fissure.

5. *Activation of the face* (by attachment of fascia lata fibres to temporal muscle flap.)

2. Hemiatrophy of the face (unilateral lipodystrophy): condition improved by insertion of fat grafts.

> *Proc. Roy. Soc. Med.*, 27, i, 1933-4 pp. 642-643

3. Three cases of facial paralysis treated by temporal muscle graft and fascia lata control.

> *Proc. Roy. Soc. Med.*, 27, ii, 1933-4, pp. 1382-1384

4. The development and scope of plastic surgery.

> *Northwest Univ. Bull. Med. Sch.*, 35, 1935, pp. 1-32

This was the Charles H Mayo Lecture. The periodical is not available.

5. Experiences with tubed pedicle flaps.

> *Surg. Gynec. Obstet.*, 60, 1935, pp. 291-303

A discussion of the uses of tubed pedicle flaps.

6. Plastic surgery of the eyelids and conjunctival sacs.

Trans. Ophthal. Soc. U.K., 55, 1935, pp. 357-373.

Review of the methods of repair of the eyelid.

7. Reconstruction surgery - the repair of superficial injuries.

Surg. Gynec. Obstet., 60, 1935, pp. 559-567

1. *Classification:*
   > *Group I*: Cases in which new tissue is grafted.
   > *Group II*: Cases in which there is displacement but no true loss of tissue.
   > *Group III*: Cases in which existing tissues are altered for cosmetic purposes.

2. *Causative Agencies:*
   > *In Group I*: Burns, gunshot injuries, industrial injuries, mining accidents, road accidents.
   > *In Group II*: Accidents of transport, sports injuries.

3. *Diagnosis*

4. *Treatment plan* depends upon age, condition of health, and sex.

5. *Methods of Repair:*
   > *In Group I*: Free grafts and flaps.
   > *In Group II*: Repositioning of displaced tissues both soft and hard.

8. Treatment of lymphoedema by plastic operation; a preliminary report.

Gillies and F.R. Fraser, *BMJ*, 1935, I, pp. 96-98

A description of one case of chronic and idiopathic lymphoedema of both legs in a female aged 28 treated by plastic operations.

On admission both legs were permanently flexed at the knees, all other treatment had failed and she requested amputation.
Query inguinal block.

1st Operation:
Incision 7" long made on flexor aspect of left fore-arm down to deep fascia. Cross incisions made at the extremities of main incision to form a flap. Similar incisions were made on the left thigh extending onto the abdomen.

The deep fascia of the forearm was brought to lie on the subcutaneous tissue of the thigh. The thigh flap was sutured to the arm, and the arm flap to the thigh.

Two weeks later the swelling of the left leg had subsided considerably.

2nd Operation:
The anastomosis had been satisfactory, the lymph from the leg draining into the axilla.

A long flap was marked out on the arm continuous with the flap already in situ. This was raised. A raw area was made continuous with the abdominal defect already created and extended to the submammary region. The skin from this area was made into a flap and was sutured to the arm defect caused by raising the long flap. As much of the arm flap as possible was brought into contact with the abdomen.

3rd Operation:

Remaining portions of flap were undermined and adhesions between the abdomen and arm freed.

4th Operation:

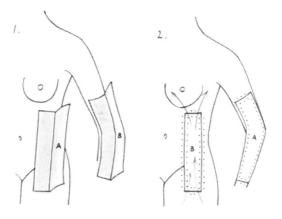

The two flaps were severed, the arm flap interchanged with the thigh flap, and both sutured in place.

Discussion:

Operation proved that separate surface lymphatic systems can be surgically united.

9. The role of plastic surgery in burns due to roentgen rays and radium.

Gillies and McIndoe, *Ann. Surg.*, 101, 1935, pp. 979-996

Vide: 2935-1934, 3, above. No additions are made.

———————————

1936 – 1938

1. Prognosis in plastic surgery

Gillies and Rainsford Mowlem,
Lancet, II, 1936, pp. 1346-1347, 1411-1412

Congenital defects:

1. Cleft lip and/or palate
2. Moles and naevi
3. Congenital limb conditions

Summary:
The great majority of congenital lesions or defects can be eliminated or materially improved. In most instances treatment should begin early in life. This will assure the best possible result from the physical standpoint, and will reduce to a minimum secondary psychological traumata.

Acquired defects:

1. Abrasions
2. Wounds
3. Tissue loss
4. Fractures

2. Reconstruction of the external ear with special reference to the use of maternal ear cartilage as the supporting structure.

Rev. Chir. Struct., 1937, pp. 169-179

Covering:

Skin transferred to site by

1.   Local rotation flaps
2.   Tubed pedicle flap.

Support:

1.   Preserved human ear cartilage
2.   Cartilage from other sources, i.e. rib
3.   Preserved ox cartilage
4.   Maternal ear cartilage
5.   Osteo-periosteal flap from mastoid region.

3. Treatment of facial paralysis

Trans. Med. Soc. Lond., 60, 1937, pp. 170-171, 179

Temporal muscle flap attached to fascia lata sling.

Vide I 1933-1935, 1, above.

4. *Die Deformitaten der syphilitischen Sattenase*

> *Dtsch. Z. Chir.*, 250, 1938, pp. 379-401

The address given at the annual meeting of the Berlin Medical Society, 1938.

5. Syphilitic destruction of nasal contour: restoration by intranasal skin grafting.

> *Rev. Chir. Struct.*, 8, 1938, pp. 31-32

Vide: 1923, 8, above.

6. The primary treatment of facial injuries.

> *Practitioner*, 140, 1938, pp. 414-425

Review of the methods of promoting good primary healing.

1939 – 1942

1. Practical uses of the tubed pedicle flap.

Amer. J. Surg., N.J. 43, 1939, pp. 201-215

Conditions in which a tubed flap is preferable to a free graft:
1. *Scalp*. Complete avulsion with exposure of bone.
2. *Massive whole facial reconstruction.*
3. *Nose*. When the forehead flap method is unavailable or undesired.
4. *Cheeks*. Large repairs where soft, supple skin is desired with restoration of contour.
5. *Lips and Chin*. In total loss following excision for disease and in burn contractures.
6. *Neck*. All severe losses of skin.
7. *Front of Chest* In cases where good cosmetic result is desired.
8. *Back of Trunk*. Free grafts are indicated except in shoulder region.
9. *Upper Limb*. Burn and contraction of forearm. Direct flap usually employed.
10. *Hand*. Where repair involves opening of joint cavity, tubed pedicle preferable.
11. *Lower Limb*. In defects limiting movement of knee joint and ankle, tubed pedicle is transferred from abdomen via wrist.

Common donor sites for tubed pedicles:

1. *Oblique Inguinial.* Safe flap with arm as intermediary host.
2. *Acromiopectoral.* Safe flap particularly suited to nasal and facial restoration having finer skin than abdomen.
3. *Scapula Region.* Donor site for grafts to back of neck and for axillary repairs.
4. *Front of Arm.* Satisfactory donor site for facial and nasal repairs. It leaves objectionable scar on the arm.
5. *Vertical Abdominal.* Used via wrist for transportation anywhere, or it can climb by the jump method.
6. *Thoraco-epigastric.* Extension of oblique inguinal particularly useful in repairs of defects of upper arm including axilla.
7. *Vertical Neck.* Good method of transporting skin to lower half of neck. It has been largely superseded by the acromiopectoral.
8. *Many other donor sites* are available but the commonest chosen are the abdominal or acromiopectoral.

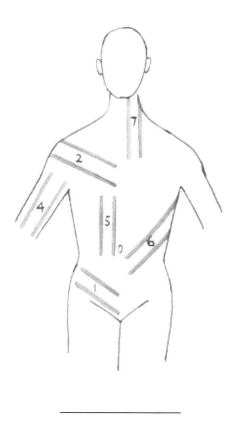

2. The techniques of mammaplasty in conditions of hypertrophy of the breast.

Surg. Gynec, Obstet., 68, 1939, pp. 658-665

Types of mammary hypertrophy:

1. Long, flabby, pendulous breasts in young girl of normal build; of hereditary or endocrine origin.

2. Broad, heavy breasts develop with obesity and pregnancy.
3. Sac-like dependent breasts following obesity reduction and pregnancy.
4. True gynaecomastia – uncommon.
5. Asymmetry.

Indications for operation:

1. Symptoms produced by weight of breasts.
2. Painful breasts.
3. Limitation of social activities.
4. Psychic disturbances.

Pre-operative preparation:

On the evening before operation entire thorax, upper part of abdomen and arms are prepared with ether, soap and spirit. The whole area is painted with acriflavine solution 1:1000 and covered with a sterile jacket. The treatment is repeated on the operating table.

Operating Principles:

Two methods of reducing breast tissue:

1. Resection of lateral half of the breast preserving the perforating branches of the internal mammary artery to form an internal pedicle with nipple and areola near the most dependent portion.

2. Resection of the upper and middle portion of the breast to form a U-shaped pedicle and carrying the nipple at the apex of the U.

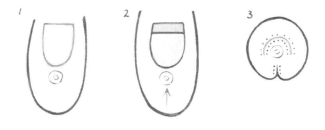

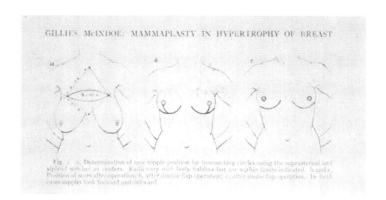

GILLIES McINDOE: MAMMAPLASTY IN HYPERTROPHY OF BREAST

Fig. 2. 3. Determination of new nipple position by intersecting circles using the suprasternal and xiphoid notches as centers. Radii vary with body habitus but are within limits indicated. b and c, Position of scars after operation; b, after double flap operation; c, after single flap operation. In both cases nipples look forward and outward.

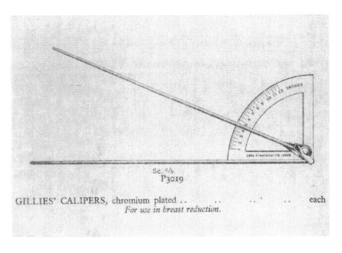

Sc. ²/₃
P3019

GILLIES' CALIPERS, chromium plated ..   ..   each
For use in breast reduction.

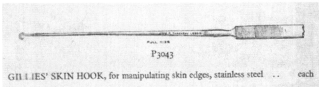

P3043

GILLIES' SKIN HOOK, for manipulating skin edges, stainless steel   ..   each

Complications:

1. Haemorrhage
2. Sepsis
3. Partial necrosis of flaps or pedicles.

General Prognosis:

There would appear to be no question as to the satis-factory end-results of this operation.

3. Autograft of amputated digit: a suggested operation.

Lancet, 1940, I, pp. 1002-1003

Rationale:

Grafts of whole fingers unsuccessful because of initial lack of blood supply to subcutaneous tissue and skin. Bone and tendon require but little blood supply: therefore can be grafted successfully.

Technique:

Amputated finger is thoroughly cleansed and dissected free of subcutaneous tissue, muscle and skin. The tendons are united with those of the hand and the bone ends are held in correct position by a few silk or catgut sutures.

A subcutaneous pocket is made on the abdomen into which the denuded finger is introduced.

After a minimal period of three weeks a flap of skin to eventually cover the finger is partly raised around the buried finger. The final division takes place a week afterwards and the flap is sewn around the finger.

Alternative Procedure:

The bone and tendons of the amputated finger could be stored indefinitely in an abdominal pouch.

4. *Cirurgia Plastica.*

> *Rev. Assoc. Med. Argent.*, 56, 1942, pp. 196-198

An introduction to plastic surgery.

5. Technique in construction of an auricle.

> *Trans. Amer. Aced. Ophthal* (1941), 46, 1942, pp. 119-121

Vide: 1936-1935, 2, above

6. Radiotherapy in the prophylaxis and treatment
of keloid.

> Gillies and WM Levitt, *Lancet*, 1942, I, pp. 440-442

Radiation is to be given to patients in which keloid is likely
to occur, before operation.

Indications and Contra-indications:

1. *Prevention of keloid*: combined and pre- and post-opera-
    tive treatment. Prophylatic irradiation should be car-
    ried out in all cases where -
i. the patient is known to have keloid-forming tenden-
    cies
ii. the incision is across natural skin creases
iii. an incision has to be made in thick skin
iv. there has been continued exposure of raw surfaces, as
    in burns

2. *Treatment of developed keloid*: those that do best are red fleshy type. Treatment for hard, extensive keloid has to be persistent. Well-developed white fibrous thickenings are completely radio-resistant.

3. *Contra-indications*: presence of acute inflammatory lesions such as boils or sepsis in the neighbourhood of the scar: in case of young woman with abdominal scars.

Method:

Localised application with production of erythematous reaction.

Facial scars 10% lower dosage than those on body. Smallest scars may be given 1500 r at first exposure.

Larger areas of scarring, according to size, may be given between 800 and 1000 r.

Six weeks should ideally elapse between first and second doses.

Three methods of application:

i. Contact therapy
ii. Medium voltage therapy (130-150 kV)
iii. High voltage therapy (200 kV).

No special apparatus is required, and although contact therapy is a convenient method of treatment for smaller scars and for prophylaxis cases, it is by no means essential. Any reliable X- ray therapy apparatus will serve provided it is accurately calibrated.

———————————

1943 – 1945

1. A new free graft applied to the reconstruction of the nostril.

Brit. J. Surg., 30, 1942-3, pp. 305-307

Rationale and Method:

Normal nostril is lined by a very thin piece of skin closely adherent to a thin piece of cartilage. Such a thin piece of skin and cartilage is readily available in the concha of the ear.

The conchal graft is taken *in toto* and buried beneath the flap to be eventually swung onto the nose, either on the forehead or the chest.

Example:

Mrs LO, aged 33 years, had her nose bitten off by a dog on 8th August 1941.

First operation (14th August): implantation of chondro- cutaneous graft in forehead.

Second operation (17th September): forehead flap with new-made ala brought into position on nose.

Third operation (3rd October): return of forehead flap pedicle.

Fourth operation (8th January 1942): nasal trimming.

2. Plastic surgery of burns of the hand.

Gillies and J.B. Cuthbert, *Med. Ann.*, 1943, pp. 259-263

Types of Skin Destruction:

1. *Full-thickness destruction* - healing takes place by centripetal invasion of the epithelial edge.
2. *Partial dermal destruction* - healing takes place by rapid epithelialization from deep glandular layers.

Treatment of Healed Palmar Burns
Radical excision of scarring with application of full-thickness graft to area.

Treatment of Healed Dorsal Burns
Excision of scarring, mobilization of skin and division of transverse metacarpal ligaments, followed by 'thick split skin- grafts' applied to area.

Burns involving the deep tissues are treated as above.

Treatment of Flexion Deformity of the Proximal
  Interphalangeal Joint
1. Meticulous dissection and excision of all scar tissue.
2. Anterior capsulotomy.
3. Division of the lateral ligaments.
4. Application of thick-skin grafts.

Operation of Pollicization of the Index Finger
Transposition of the index finger with lengthening and dis-

placement of the two extensor tendons of the index finger to facilitate apposition.

Stage 1: Index metacarpal divided at the junction of proximal and middle thirds. The distal fragment was wired in apposition with the thumb metacarpal.

Stage 2: Interdigital cleft between index and middle fingers was split. Index finger was then widely abducted and palmar and dorsal skin flaps were utilised to cover the medial side of the interdigital cleft between the new thumb and the middle finger.

Result:
After division of the tendon of extensor indices proprius and lengthening of extensor digitorum communis tendon to new thumb, abduction, adduction and apposition could be achieved.

3. Plastic surgery of facial injuries.

Gillies and Cuthbert, *Med. Ann.*, 1943, pp. 263-266

Types of facial injury and a review of their treatment.

4. Technique of good suturing.

St Barts. Hosp. J., 47, 1943-4, pp. 170-173

5. Note on scalp closure.

Lancet, 1944, II, pp. 310-311

Methods recommended:

1.   Sliding rotation flap
2.   Curved tripod
3.   Relaxation incisions.

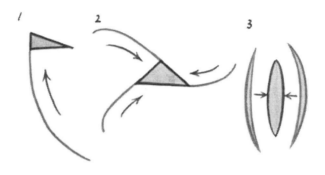

6. Operative replacement of the mammary prominence.

Brit. J. Surg., 32, 1944-5, pp. 477-479

Technique:
Method consists of transferring the circum-umbilical skin and fat pad by means of a tubed pedicle to form the 'breast'. The umbilicus is turned out to form the 'nipple'.

Stage 1: Pedicle designed with root situated in mid-axillary line at the level of the 6th rib. Part of the pedicle is raised.

Stage 2: After two weeks the remaining part of the pedicle is raised together with part of the circum-umbilical flap. The 'nipple' is supported with acrylic or cartilage button.

The raw areas left by these operations are covered with full thickness grafts.

Stage 3: After two weeks the remaining abdominal attachment is divided and pedicle is raised to the recipient area.

Stage 4: Three weeks later the pedicle is returned leaving the flap in situ as new breast.

7. Late end-results of war burns.

Trans. Med. Soc. Lond., 63 (1940-43), 1945, pp. 134-136

A review of 'follow-ups' of burns cases after plastic surgery.

Operative Replacement of Mammary Prominence

A case of Radioneceosis.

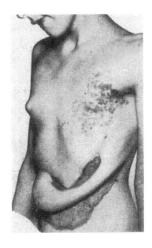

Pedicle to umbilical region raised and prepared

Implementation of the flap after excision of the scarring.

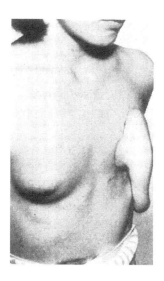

*Left breast reconstructed: right breast
ptosed after lactation.*

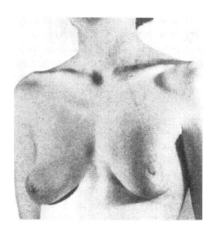

1946 – 1952

1. Congenital absence of penis, with embryological considerations.

Gillies and R.J. Harrison,
Brit. J. Plast Surg., 1, 1948-49, pp. 8-28

In the case under discussion there was no penis but there were two perfectly normal testicles in their scrotum. On investigation there was no sexual prominence to be found and no opening in the perineum except the anus. The urethral opening was found 1 inch inside the anal canal.

The patient was 16 years old when he was sent for an opinion. He had micturated twice a day *per rectum* and had been able to control the flow.

Operation:

1. The proctologist dissected the urethra from the rectum.
2. The urologist introduced the urethra through the perineum.
3. The plastic surgeon had raised a 12" tubed pedicle from the abdomen which enclosed a narrow-bored cylinder of epithelium to act as the urethra of the penis. The

freed end of the pedicle was swung down and introduced through the walls of the scrotum to lie in the
normal anatomical position of the shaft. The normal
urethra was sutured to the false urethra and the head
of the pedicle to the perineum.

*In a later operation the root of the penis was detached and was
trimmed to form the new 'glans'. A cartilage implant was made.*

2. Team Surgery in Cancer.

Proc. Roy. Soc. Med., 42, 1949, pp. 176-183

Presentation of eight cases illustrating cooperation between general and plastic surgeon.

The general surgeon should not be influenced in the extent of his excision by any consideration of cosmetic effect. The plastic surgery team should repair the defect immediately the excision has been completed.

This arrangement would lessen the psychological traumata suffered by cases having undergone amputation of breast or penis, or radical excision in the facial region.

3. Reconstruction of the ear and nose.

In Carling and Ross, *British Surgical Practice*,Vol.7, 1950, pp.298-318

Account of methods available for restoration of the nose and ear auricle.

4. Operative correction by osteotomy of recessed malar maxillary compound in case of oxycephaly.

Gillies and SH Harrison, *Brit. J. Plast Surg.*, 3, 1950-51, pp.123-127

The patient exhibited characteristics of craniostenosis: proptosis, under-development of maxilla, high arch to palate and nose that was approximated to upper lip. On x-ray examination there was evidence of premature stenosis of the cranial sutures and a high vault of the skull with a peak at the bregma.

Operations: After arrest of the condition had been confirmed,

1. The malar-maxillary component of the skull, with palate and septum nasi attached, was detached, pulled forward and down to a normal position and held with inter-maxillary wiring.
2. Seven years later the proptosis was treated by removal of middle third of the floor of the orbit and application of ox cartilage blocks to the malar regions.

5. Ox cartilage in plastic surgery.

Brit. J. Plast Surg., 4, 1951-52, pp. 63-73

Ox cartilage is not fragile and possesses an exceptional range of elasticity. It causes no visible reaction in human tissues; it is apparently inert. It maintains the shape that has been fashioned by the operator, but is very susceptible to exposure and haematoma infection.

Introduction of bovine cartilage into the human tissues in a diced or minced state is unsatisfactory as the phagocytic elements quickly absorb it. In block form, however, the cartilage will remain unaltered for long periods of time.

6. *Cirurgia plastica.*

Rev. Samid. Milit. Argent., 51, 1952, pp. 89-93

7. Local use of chloramphenicol in wound infections.

Gillies, MH Flint and DAC Reid, *Lancet*,
1952, I. pp. 541-544

1.   *Account of reports published on the uses of chloramphenicol ('Chloromycetin').*

2. *Present Investigation:*

Local applications of 5% chloramphenicol, either as a powder in lactose or as a solution in propylene glycol, were used to obtain a rapid bacterial clearance of a wide variety of wounds infected by penicillin-resistant or insensitive organisms.

The chief organisms encountered were ps. pyocyanea, proteus vulgaris, and penicillin-resistant and streptomycin-resistant staph. aureus. All but one case (of the thirty investigated) were sensitive to 2.5% chloramphenicol. No organism became more resistant during or after treatment.

The bacterial clearance in thirty cases was obtained in an average time of 4 or 5 days; in many cases the time was shorter, especially in cases treated with chloramphenicol in propylene glycol, which seemed more effective than a powder containing the same concentration of chloramphenicol.

―――――――――――

1953 – 1959

1. Plastic surgery.

Med. Ill., (Lond.), 7, 1953, pp. 396-402

A review of practical applications of plastic surgery.

2. Autograft of amputated digit.

Gillies and DAC Reid, *Brit. J. Plast. Surg.*, 7,
1954-55, pp. 338-342

Vide: 1939 – 1942, 3

This is a report of completed and successful cases.

3. Survival of finger nail following
digital autograft.

Gillies and DAC Reid,
Brit. J. Plast. Surg., 8, 1955-56, p. 174

4. My most interesting case. The naval on the knee.

Practitioner, 177, 1956, pp. 512-515

5. *Zpusoby Uzavreni Patrovych Defektu Novou Tkanf Tkaki.*

Acta Chir. Dethop. Traum. Cech., 24, 1957, pp. 440-442

An account of methods available for closure of a maxillary defect with new tissue.

6. The Principles and Art of Plastic Surgery

by Sir Harold Gillies and Dr Ralph Millard. Chapter on anaesthetics by Sir Ivan Magill. Foreword by Dr Jerome P. Webster.

Published by Little, Brown and Co., Boston, 1957

Volume I

I.   THE FIRST ACT   CINDERELLA SURGERY

1.   World War One:- the origins of plastic surgery
2.   Principles
3.   Anaesthesia by Sir Ivan Magill
4.   Technical Tips
5.   Skin Grafting
6.   Inlay Grafting

II. FLAP HAPPY

Volume II

III. PRIVATE PRACTICE

IV. PRIVATE PRACTICE

27. Fractures of the Malar-Zygomatic Compound
28. Nasal Fractures
29. Frontal Defects
30. Eyelids and Sockets
31. Facial Paralysis
32. Cross-grafting

V. FINAL SCENE

33. A Day in the Clinic

This book is a distillation of the entire life work of Sir Harold Gillies.

7. The 'periwinkleshell' principle in the treatment of the small ptotic breast

Gillies and H Marino,
Plast. Reconstr. Surg., 21, 1958, pp. 1-7

1. *Causes of ptotic or flat, discoid breasts:*
   1. Senility
   2. Endocrine involution
   3. Reduction of obesity
   4. Pregnancies.

2. *Fractures of ptotic breasts:*
   1. Descent of nipples below the xiphoid line
   2. Lack of fullness, particularly in the upper quadrants
   3. Lack of firmness.

3. *Surgical treatment:*

    The gland is liberated from the skin starting from an inverted T-incision. Three procedures are then available:

    1. A flap is made above nipple and the glandular substances raised and sutured in place.

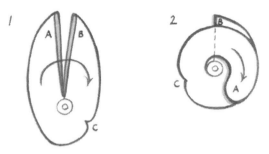

    2. A wedge is made below nipple, and the tissues sewn over it.

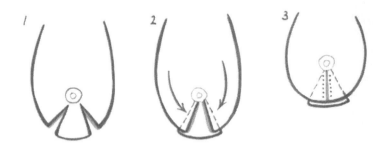

    3. The authors believe that the rotation method is most satisfactory morphologically and aesthetically.

A lateral flap is made and freed from underlying fascia. The flap is revolved around the nipple and is sutured to the medial lower quadrant of the remaining glandular tissue. The whole reshaped breast is sutured to the pectoral fascia.

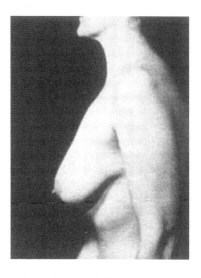

Ptotic breasts before treatment.

Ptotic breasts after 'periwinkle-shell' operation

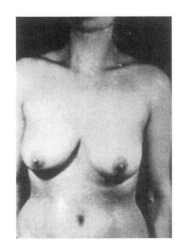
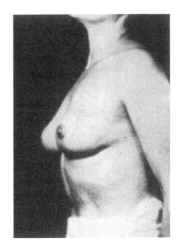

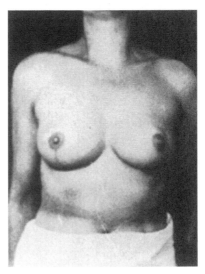

8. Plastic surgery in naval cases.

J. Roy. Nav. Med. Serv., 45, 1959, pp. 7-46

1. *Editorial consisting of tribute to Sir Harold Gillies.*
2. *An account of plastic surgery with special reference to the Royal Navy by Sir Harold Gillies.*

9. Surgical replacement of the breast

Proco. Roy. Soc. Med. f 52, 1959, pp. 597-602

Vide: 1943-1945, 6, above.

This synopsis of the works of Sir Harold Gillies is based on the Bibliography, *The Writings of Sir Harold Gillies*, by John L. Thornton, Esq, (*St Barts. Hosp. J.*, LXX, 3, 1961)

———————————